PORRIDGE

Oats & Their Many Health Benefits

PORRIDGE

Oats & Their Many Health Benefits

Margaret Briggs

Abbeydale Press

ISBN 978-1-86147-069-0

9 10 8

Published by Abbeydale Press
an imprint of Bookmart Ltd
Registered number 2372865
Trading as Bookmart Ltd
Blaby Road, Wigston, Leicester
LE18 4SE, England

Produced for Bookmart Limited
Illustrations by Tegan Sharrard, Omnipress Limited, UK
Cover design by Vivian Foster

Printed in Dubai

ABOUT THE AUTHOR

Margaret Briggs was a teacher for 30 years, working in Kent,
Germany, North Yorkshire and Sussex. She has always enjoyed
gardening and has grown plants both to eat and look at for all
her adult life.

Since leaving teaching she has had more time for gardening and
cooking and has embarked on a second career as a freelance
writer, researcher and editor, alongside her writer husband, Lol.
Six years ago the couple bought a dilapidated house in SW
France. The house is now restored and Margaret and Lol divide
their time between Sussex and the Gironde, with two
contrasting gardens to develop.

Margaret has written two more books in this series, *Vinegar
1001 Practical Uses* was published in 2005 and *Gardening Hints
and Tips* in 2006.

CONTENTS

Introduction

I hadn't realised before I started compiling this book how emotive an object a bowl of porridge could be. Who could imagine that a few basic ingredients could create such cultural differences: who could foretell that there are so many ways of preparing a humble, or not so humble breakfast? Everyone I mention porridge to has a very firm view on the product; you either love it or hate the stuff.

I've vaguely known about the properties of oatmeal in connection with face packs from my teenage years, but the width and depth of beauty treatments made possible by the inclusion of oats is quite staggering. Festivals and events are held worldwide in the pursuit of the perfect bowl of porridge, and rather than lose momentum over the years have actually gained a new impetus.

The heralding of porridge oats as a major health food and the introduction of the Glycaemic Index have added weight to the health benefits of getting back to basic, wholegrain recipes. Celebrity consumers and chefs are constantly singing its praises. Throughout history, armies have marched on it and multitudes have slept on it or fed their horses on it.

There are countless references in literature to porridge, although some of the language it invokes does have the air of a porringer full of overcooked oats. Maybe some of the authors were not aware of the origins of sowing wild oats, or were not 'getting their oats'.

This book sets out to pull together a number of facts, some whimsical, some deadly serious, about oats. It gives helpful suggestions as to how best to consume them, whether with whipped cream, salt, butter, snails or any ingredient of your choice; whatever grabs you.

Best thing since sliced porridge!

Know Your Oats

Oats are produced from edible, starchy grains from the oat plant *Avena Sativa*, not to be confused with oat grasses. Arrhenatherum includes six species of tall grasses which are native to Europe and Asia and have been used as pasture grasses for animal grazing. Danthonia is a group of 100 species, all native to the southern hemisphere; they are particularly prolific in Australia, New Zealand and South American countries. In Australia oat grass is known as wallaby grass. Unfortunately, you wouldn't make much of a porridge from these plants.

Oats are annual plants which grow, flower and seed before dying in the autumn. The word 'oat' refers to both the plant and the grain. The exact number of species of *Avena Sativa* is unknown, but is estimated to be fewer than 50. The porridge oats we eat today were first found in western Europe as wild oats, or a weed growing with barley. The usefulness of these cereals for both human and animal foodstuffs quickly became apparent and oats spread around the world. Now known as common oats, they grow in cool temperate climates. Red oats, originating in the Mediterranean region, are more heat tolerant and are grown in warmer climates. Wild red oats are considered to be weeds in most grain producing countries, but their properties, including resistance to rust spores and high yields, make them valuable plants for producing hybrid varieties.

SCATTER!
The problem with wild oats is that the seeds ripen quickly and scatter from the parent plant before harvesting is possible. This is an obvious disadvantage for farmers and may give us a clue as to the origin of the expression 'sowing one's wild oats' (see page 44). Oats have an awn, which is a long bristle-like tail at the tip of the lowest bract underneath the flower. The awn's function is to help the seed to plant itself. The wild red has a different awn from other varieties and twists with changing conditions, depending on weather conditions and humidity.

NO FLIES ON AVENA!
The movement of the awn pushes the seed into the ground to anchor it in the soil. This twisting reverses in dry weather so that the awn can untwist and revert to its original mode. Fishermen soon noticed this unique property and began to make flies from one or two awns tied together. Thus the 'fly' attracts fish, as it mimics the movements of insects landing on the water.

Avena Sativa has a flowering and fruiting structure made up of a number of branches bearing florets. These produce the caryopsis, or one-seeded fruits, of whose aphrodisiac qualities you will read more later! (page 33)

WHO NEEDS THEM?
Oats are not classified as demanding plants and are second only to rye in their ability to adapt and survive in poor soil structures. They compete well with other cereals in poor soils and in short wet growing seasons. They will grow in sandy soils, highly acidic soils or any which are generally low in fertility. Areas of greatest production are concentrated in Europe, particularly in Sweden, Finland, Russia, Poland and Germany, and also in the USA, Canada and Australia. Canadian production remains fairly high.

HARVEST FOR THE WORLD?
World oats production in 2002/03 of 26.7 million tons compared with 27 million a year earlier and an average of about 30 million metric tons in the mid-1990s. Globally, average yields show wide divergence, from as low of less than 1.5 tons per acre at times in Russia and China to almost 5 tons per acre in Western Europe, notably in France. Russia remains one of the largest producers with about 8.2 million tons in 2002/03, nearly a third of the world's total, owing to the large acreage they are able to devote to oats. Among the few major producers Canada has shown relative steadiness in production during the past decade, averaging about 3.2 million tons, although lower yields in 2002/03 dropped production to about 2.9 million tons.

As world oat production has halved in the last 30 years, it now stands at about 25 million tons. Over this same period, world production of all grains has doubled at the expense of oats, which have tended to be squeezed out of crop rotations by other, higher yielding cereal crops. Most of the world's oats production is consumed domestically and world trade is small. In 2002/03 exports were forecast at 2.23 million tons vs. 1.83 million in 2001/02, with Canada accounting for almost half the total, namely 950,000 tons. Importing nations are more numerous, but the U.S. is the consistent leader with 1.75 million tons in 2002/03 vs. 1.4 million in 2001/02.

HAY FOR HORSES

In many countries the grains are used mainly as livestock feed, either in pure or mixed form. Oats provide straw for animal bedding and good hay, grazing and silage. One of the upward turns in the oat's markets is attributable to the niche market of horse feed. Although there are far fewer working horses around in the developed world than in previous centuries, keeping horses for recreational use has increased rapidly, to compensate for the market in preferred feed for horses and ponies, especially in the USA.

P FOR PORRIDGE

In other parts of the world oats are grown on a small scale for human consumption, especially as breakfast cereal. The pattern is constantly changing, and although there has been a decline in oat production for many years, the trend has changed again more recently, due to recognition of the various health benefits to be gained from eating porridge. In the UK 40% of the oats consumed find their way into porridge and oatmeal products. Oat grains are high in fibre and carbohydrates and contain 13% protein and only 6.9% fat. They are a source of calcium, iron, vitamin B and nicotinic acid. More recent figures show that the downward trend in European oat production has been reversed, with Sweden and Finland providing 40% of Europe's crop. Human consumption is on the increase in other parts of northern Europe as well, so perhaps the trend will grow and I'll be able to buy oats in south west France soon!

INDUSTRIAL APPLICATIONS

Another, less well known use of oat hulls is as a source of furfural, a chemical used in the production of various types of oily solvents. The dried hulls are rich in carbon sugars. Furfural is used in the refining of lubricating oils, in the manufacture of shoe dyes, herbicides and fungicides, and in the production of nylon.

Oat flour is used as a preservative on the inner coatings of paper bags for salted peanuts, coffee and crisps. It contains antioxidants which prevent fat-containing foods, such as peanut butter, margarine, chocolate and doughnuts, from going rancid. Oat flour also stabilises fats in ice cream and other dairy products. If reconstituted with water, oat flour forms a gel for use in salad dressings, gravies, dips, soups, coatings and drink mixes. These gels can also replace fat in baked products.

OATS, GROATS, FLAKES AND BRAN

Groats are unflattened kernels with their husks or hulls removed. *Oatmeal* is made by grinding groats into pieces of varying texture from coarse to fine. *Rolled oats* are produced by steaming and flattening the kernels and removing the husks to make oatmeal. Rolled oats cook faster than steel-cut oats and are better for modern porridge making. *Oat flour* is unsuitable for making bread, but is used to make biscuits and puddings. *Steel-cut oats* have a dense and chewy texture, produced by running the grain through steel blades which slice them thinly.

Oats contain 70 to 75 percent groat, which is milled into steel-cut oats, rolled flakes, instant flakes, flour and bran. The remaining hull is waste, but can be burned for energy.

Much of early man's nutrition came from grain which had a tightly fitting husk. The only way to remove it was to burn it off. The resulting toasted grain had much better storage qualities than untoasted grains.

Naked oats have been developed which have a loose hull that is blown away during combining. The crude protein, oil and energy content of the hull-less variety is much greater than ordinary oats. Storage costs are lower, so it is well suited for some speciality food markets. However, yields are lower and because the skin coat is thinner, the oats can be damaged during combining, leading to rancidity problems in storage and reduced shelf life. About 90 percent of US oats are grown for livestock feed and industrial uses.

ROLL ME AN OAT, PLEASE

Oats get their distinctive flavour from being roasted after harvesting and cleaning. Since hulling the oats doesn't strip away their bran and germ, they retain the concentration of fibre and nutrients. Over the years they have been milled in different ways. Old-fashioned oats have a flatter shape that is the result of their being steamed and then rolled. You can find out a lot more about processed oats in later sections, but you should be aware that many instant oat products don't have the same beneficial qualities as more natural ones.

The History Behind a Bowl of Porridge

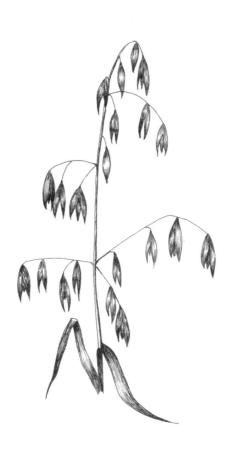

SUPERGRASS

10,000 years ago people first started to collect grains. By the end of the last ice age, Man was better organised and had the technology to challenge changes to the environment. Rainfall distribution and sea level changes led to a greater use of grasses and three major groups of cereals were collected, then cultivated, in different parts of the world. Neolithic farmers cultivated oats along with other crops. They used various types of grains and meals stewed in water to form a thick porridge-like dish.

CEREAL THRILLER

In Europe, India and the Near East wheat, barley and oats predominated, although evidence has also been found of oat cultivation in Chinese civilisations thousands of years ago. The oldest oat grains found have been dated to the 12th dynasty in Egypt. The ancient Greeks also made a type of porridge from oats but, as it was not considered an important food source, used it in medicines. Hippocrates, the father of medicine, recommended oats after acute fevers and in convalescence.

Even then oats were counted as a sure way of fortifying the body and the Romans knew all about their qualities, too. Talking about oat bread, Pliny the Elder (c AD 23-79) apparently said: 'This bread, from which we live, contains almost countless remedies.' The Romans also used oats, however, as an important source of nutrition for its armies, marching across Europe. They also introduced the scythe for harvesting cereals, straw and hay crops. The straw retained enough nutrition to double up as hay for cattle in times of need. The husks were easier to remove after burning and from toasted grains people produced pastes by mixing the crushed, toasted grain with water to form a sort of dumpling. This could be eaten without baking and was quick to prepare. Toasting made the grain digestible. Grain pastes were a major part of the diet of the poor through Roman times, especially in cities where the hazard of fire prevented many people from cooking in their homes.

China and South East Asia cultivated mainly millet and rice, which thrived on the climate. In Central America wild forms of maize were developed. This type of regional cultivation accounts for the reason why today porridge is made from a variety of cereals. Wherever people lived and communities evolved, flat grinding stones, or saddle querns, have been found. These were needed to process the hard grains to make porridge or flour.

WHAT'S BREWING?

The Anglo Saxons made porridge from rye, barley and oats and their tribes probably introduced porridge to Britain. This porridge, called 'briw', was served either plain or with vegetables added. These included cabbage, parsnips and carrots, which were introduced by the Romans. Some porridges were fermented, so perhaps that's where we get the word for a brew. It must have been quite difficult to prevent fermentation taking place, since storage conditions would have been somewhat haphazard. A warm moist spell could wreak havoc with cereals.

Porridges were easy to cook and had an advantage over bread, in that you didn't need to have an oven or grind grains to make flour. You only had to crack the grains and cook them in a pot on the edge of a fire.

TOP CROP

By 1086, twenty years after the Battle of Hastings and the start of the Norman Conquest, 80% of all the land which would eventually be farmed by 1914 was already in agricultural use. The survey of land use carried out for the Domesday Book recorded that 35% of land was under arable use and 25% was pasture. Landowners were rich and the population was growing fast. Land was mostly cultivated on a rotation of two to three years. In 1100, arable crops would be grown for up to ten years without a fallow break, rendering the soil fairly infertile. Peas and beans were grown which acted as a fertiliser for cereal crops and, although wheat grown as the main bread crop and rye was popular in dry areas of the country, oats remained widespread throughout the uplands and on less fertile soil. Barley was grown for malt and brewing.

Fertility was measured by the number of ploughs per square mile, with areas of Sussex and Hertfordshire leading the table with four ploughs. Poorer areas, such as the north and the Somerset levels, recorded only one. The Domesday Book also records 6000 mills in operation for grinding grain, all of which were water mills. It was not until the 12th century that windmills were introduced to Britain.

A STEW BY ANY OTHER NAME
In medieval times cooking took place over a fire which was constantly fed. The diet of mostly vegetables and grains with a little meat was usually stewed over the fire, with leftovers remaining in the pot overnight. You can imagine the build up of bacteria over time, as oatmeal has quite a reputation for harbouring unpleasant micro-organisms. Those on the edge of starvation made use of every scrap, re-cooking the stew for breakfast and adding ingredients when possible. A stew of grains, vegetables, water and bacon scraps became known as 'pottage' (which is very close to the French 'potage', a kind of soup).

When I told my brother I was writing this book, he told me about a midnight foraging trip he undertook whilst camping with a scouts' troop about 40 years ago. He decided he would finish off the porridge from breakfast that nobody had washed up. Unfortunately he was ill all next day, and since he was the only known porridge thief, there was only one conclusion to be reached. Goldilocks must have got off lightly, then! There is probably also some sense to the *Pease porridge hot* rhyme. More on this subject later.

WHEAT WITH YOUR MEAT?
From Saxon times a wheat based porridge called frumenty or furmenty was used as an accompaniment for meat or as a breakfast meal. It was made from hulled wheat and meat stock seasoned with spices. For interest I've included a recipe in a later section (page 151). Try your powers of translation on this little lot:

*Tak clene whete & braye yt wel in a mortar tyl the holes
gon of; seethe it til it breste in water.
Nym it vp & lt it cole.
Tak good broth & swete mylk of kyn or of almand &
tempere it therwith.
Nym yelkys of eyren rawe & saffroun & cast therto; salt it;
lat it naught boyle after the eyren ben cast therinne.
Messe it forth with venesoun or with fat motoun fresch.*

(Original fourteenth or fifteenth century English recipe
for frumenty)

The recipe was adapted in Norman times to include milk
and egg yolks. The rich overlords would eat frumenty
with strongly flavoured meats such as game, wild boar or
venison. Later it also formed the basis of many more
dishes, sweetened with honey, fruit, spices or vegetables.

CRUEL NOT COOL!
Gruel was a porridge made of grain, usually rolled oats
and water. It was not a very exciting or nourishing
foodstuff, but a thin concoction of a small handful of
rolled oats to five or six cups of water. Dickens made
good use of gruel as a metaphor for poverty and ill
treatment in the workhouses of Victorian Britain, but
we're getting ahead of ourselves. Gruel could be
sweetened with almond milk. A dish called Gruya was
made in medieval times with barley boiled in flavoured
milk. Burstin was made from ground, roasted barley and
also served with milk; we should remember that sugar
was not available to the masses in the eighteenth
century.

Water gruel, made from oatmeal and water and flavoured
with butter and pepper, was served in the eighteenth
century. Rich people ate it with wine, sherry or dried
fruit but the poor ate it on its own, for any meal.

GROWING OATS? A PIECE OF CAKE!

Oats became popular as a crop throughout Europe in the Middle Ages because they were easy to cultivate. There is mention from John Gerard in 1597 that:

> *'Common Otes is used in many countries to make sundry sorts of bread . . . Jannocks, Haver cakes, Tharsse cakes . . . which are called generally Oten cakes . . .'* He added: *'These naked Otes immediately, as they bethreshed, without helpe of a Mill, become Otemeale fit for our use . . . Some of those good house-wives that delight not to have anything but from hand to mouth . . . may (whiles their pot doth seeth) go to the barne and rub forth with their hands sufficient for that present time, not willing to provide for tomorrow.'*

DOCTOR OATS?

Maybe the movement for whole grain, organic foods was already getting underway in the sixteenth century, or perhaps it was a way of keeping the women in their place. The rich would not consider eating oats, which was for animal feed and medicinal use. They did use oatmeal for pain relief, apparently, by putting grains of oats into linen bags and heating them:

> *'Common Otes put into a linnen bag, with a little bay salt quilted handsomely for the same purpose, and made hot in a frying pan, and applied very hot, easeth the paine in the side callt eh stitch, or collicke in the belly.'*

So there you have it: the microwavable sack of grains for easing muscle pains isn't new at all, but another recycled idea, made simpler by the use of technology.

Oats made their way to America in the seventeenth century with Scottish New World settlers. Originally they were used there mainly as a cure for stomach ailments, but their popularity as a breakfast cereal grew. The first commercially packaged oats were sold in 1854, but sales increased with the setting up of the Quaker Oats Company in 1901. Incidentally, the owners were not Quakers at all, but the picture on the packaging still gives that impression. Originally the grains were just rolled flat, but they took a long time to cook. Nowadays, since the grain is toasted, hulled, steamed, cut and rolled, it undergoes a lot of processing.

DIG THOSE OATS!

During the Second World War the Ministry of Food, under the enforced regime of rationing, gave advice on how to make the best use of the food that was available. They gave cookery demonstrations, made radio broadcasts and distributed recipe leaflets. One such recipe for a vegetable pie, named after the Minister of Food, Lord Woolton, included oatmeal as a filler and thickener.

Traditionally, many Scots' households used to make porridge once a week and then cool it before storing it in a porridge drawer in the kitchen. This could then be served cold by the 'piece' or slice, or reheated with boiling water to reconstitute and thin it. Fuel was saved in this way, being hard to come by in the city tenements. An alternative was to fry it in a pan as required.

FOOD FOR THOUGHT

Oatmeal was a favoured porridge until the 1950s, when oat production started to decline; it wasn't until the late 1980s that studies revealed oat bran's healthy attributes. The 21st century has seen increased consumer demand for all things oaty, from ready-to-eat oat breakfast foods and traditional porridge to oat biscuits and chewy cereal bars. Recently annual sales of porridge oats have risen to 79 million pounds and appear to be matching sales figures for wheat-based breakfast cereals.

Health statistics may help to explain why Scotland has opened the world's first porridge bar, in Edinburgh. The diet of 15th century city dwellers certainly didn't contain sugary drinks, take-away/fast food, chips, pizza, burgers etc. Obesity and levels of heart disease were not causing national concern and a shortening of life expectancy. Mind you, people didn't smoke then, either!

Health
Benefits

For centuries, oat grains have been valued for their significant medicinal properties and benefits for maintaining a healthy body. As early as 400 BC ground oat was used on skin for drying and healing, and early civilisations were certainly aware of its numerous benefits.

Porridge has undergone something of a makeover in recent years, partly due to the popularity of the GI (Glycaemic Index) Diet. It is also a good source of complex carbohydrates, which release energy slowly into the bloodstream. As they are wholegrain, oats have the natural goodness that is absent from processed cereals.

UNDERSTANDING THE GLYCAEMIC INDEX

The Glycaemic Index ranks foods based on their effects on blood sugar levels. The lower the rating on the index the better it is for blood sugar levels. Only foods which contain carbohydrates appear on the index. Slowly absorbed foods have a low GI rating, so those that are more quickly absorbed get a higher rating. By choosing foods which are slowly absorbed you help to regulate blood glucose levels. This is particularly important for people who have diabetes, although there are obvious benefits for many other groups as well. The standard reference for a GI food is 100, which is the effect on blood glucose levels of a portion of food containing 50g of carbohydrate over a three hour period, compared with that of glucose or white bread. Previously, people believed that all carbohydrates had the same effects on blood glucose levels, but it is now recognised that different foods containing carbohydrates have different effects on these levels. So 50g of bread does not have the same effect as 50g of pasta.

Meals that include low GI foods allow us to absorb carbohydrates more slowly, thereby helping to maintain even glucose levels in the blood between meals. The effects can carry over into the next meal, thus aiding levels throughout the day. Slow acting foods help reduce peaks in blood glucose that often follow a meal. This can help to prevent or reduce the risk of Type 2 diabetes.

The following chart gives some idea of the different values given by various products. Bear in mind that 50g of raw oatmeal is quite a large portion, so it goes a long way!

FOOD	GI	SERVING IN GRAMS	CARB/SERVING IN GRAMS
Porridge made from raw rolled oats in water	42	250	20.3
Traditional porridge oats	51	250	20.3
Instant porridge	65	250	20.3
Stone ground medium oatmeal (raw)	59	50 (dry)	34
Porridge from steel cut oats cooked in water	52	50 (dry)	37.4

WEIGHT LOSS AND FINDING A BALANCE
Low GI foods help to control the appetite by giving you a 'full up' feeling for longer, which means that you eat less.

It is not as easy as it seems to work out the GI of a meal. You can't just read it off a chart (and immediately feel virtuous), and you can't just confine yourself to a low GI diet because that would give an unbalanced diet. For example, milk and dairy products have a low GI because of their high protein and fat content and chocolate has a medium GI, similarly due to the fat content. Crisps have a lower GI than boiled potatoes. Fat and protein slow down the absorption of carbohydrates, but as with all diets there has to be a balance. It's no good kidding yourself that because chips, fatty food and chocolate are low GI you can eat lots of them, because then you would risk heart disease. Equally, there is no point in cutting out all high GI foods. We need to strike a balance.

Lots of factors affect the GI of a food, as will processing, ripeness of fruit and varieties of vegetables. Pasta and durum wheat, along with oatmeal, have low ratings where whole grains act as a barrier that slows down the absorption of carbohydrates. Beware, however, of thinking that wholemeal bread, where the grains have been ground up, or brown rice will give the same low reading: they are high GI foods. The crucial factor is the addition of whole grain, which is why oats are so good for you. Some mixed grain breads and those with added oats on are better for you than wholemeal bread.

SOME DRAWBACKS
The index only deals with foods which contain carbo-hydrates, so is not useful for calculating all of your dietary needs.

Unfortunately, the GI of a food is not based on commonly consumed individual portions of foods. For example, carrots contain only about 7% carbohydrates, so the portion of carrots you would need to eat to 'achieve' the GI reading would be huge — about 1.5 pounds. Portions of foods like bread, which contain a higher percentage of carbohydrates, will be smaller, again reducing the overall

GI impact simply because the index is based on larger measures or portions. Therefore, if you only refer to the Glycaemic Index, you will end up overstating the effects of foods containing a small percentage of carbohydrates. Conversely, the effects of foods containing a high percentage are likely to be understated, if you use the GI as your only point of reference. Foods that are mostly water or air will not cause a surge in your blood sugar levels even if their glycaemic index is high.

This is why scientists developed the idea of Glycaemic Load. It ranks foods according to actual carbohydrate content (e.g. in a typical portion-size), as opposed to how fast a 50g amount raises blood sugar levels.

GLYCAEMIC LOADS FOR SOME COMMON OAT PRODUCTS
(NB: note the different sized portions.)

NAME OF FOOD	SERVING SIZE IN GRAMS	GL PER SERVING
Scone	25	8
Porridge oats	250	17
Oatbran bread	30	9
Muesli	30	16
Instant porridge	250	17

DIABETES

Porridge oats are high in energy yet low in fat, so a bowl of porridge is one of the best meals to start the day with. Because oats are rich in fibre and carbohydrates they help to stabilise blood sugars, therefore they are invaluable to people suffering from diabetes. Porridge leaves you feeling full for a long time so you don't crave mid-morning snacks, thus staving off mood swings. The trick is to find the right ingredients to go with it so that you don't need added/artificial sweeteners. Having been diagnosed with Type 2 diabetes, I've undertaken some experiments on my breakfast porridge with this in mind.

When I was younger and my mum made us eat porridge on winter mornings, I always found that the best bit was the spoonful of golden syrup we added. Reverting to porridge without the traditional addition of either sugar or salt is something else, and not having either full cream or semi skimmed milk is another obstacle to overcome. Help is at hand. Of course, if you're young, fit, not overweight and don't have to worry about your blood pressure or cholesterol levels: lucky you! Long may it stay that way. You can enjoy — for now — the 'Full Monty' of porridge consumption, complete with all the goodies some of us are denied. Have a drool at the recipes!

SUPERFOOD

Compared with other whole grains, oats have one of the highest concentrations of protein, calcium, iron, magnesium, zinc, copper, manganese, thiamin, folacin and vitamin E on a per gram basis. No wonder porridge is one of the five superfoods recommended by nutritionists and the health lobby! The other four are nuts, broccoli, blueberries and avocados. The challenge is to see how many meals you can incorporate them into. I've got a few ideas I tried out on unsuspecting friends (see the recipe section).

A standard portion of cooked, whole grain oats contains:

		% of recommended daily intake
Calories	145kcal	
Total fat	2.3g	
Of which	0.4g is saturated	
	0.8g is monounsaturated	
Sodium	2mg	
Carbohydrates	25g	
Fibre	4g	16
Protein	6g	12
Manganese	1.4mg	69
Thiamin	0.3mg	17
Phosphorus	178mg	18
Selenium	19mcg	27
Magnesium	56mg	14

LOWERING CHOLESTEROL, PREVENTING HEART DISEASE AND STROKES

Produced in the liver, cholesterol is a fatty substance used to digest fats. We have two types of cholesterol, one 'bad' and one 'good'. It is also found in beef, poultry and dairy products. When our bodies have more cholesterol than the body can use, the cholesterol levels in our blood rise and can lead to blocked arteries, blood clots, heart attacks and strokes. The cholesterol lowering effect of oatmeal is quite well known, having received huge publicity in the media. Oats are an important source of both soluble (55%) and insoluble (45%) dietary fibre. The soluble fibre, beta-glucan, prevents cholesterol being absorbed into the bloodstream and then carries it out of the body. A diet rich in oats for six weeks has been found to lower both blood pressure and cholesterol. About three grams of soluble fibre a day alongside a low fat diet help to lower cholesterol and prevent heart disease. One portion of oatmeal provides about two grams, so by eating a bowl of porridge for breakfast, you're nearly there already, but don't forget your five portions of fruit and vegetables as well.

A further benefit in the prevention of cardio vascular disease was recently discovered, where antioxidant compounds which are unique to oats were found to prevent damage from free radicals. When vitamin C was added to the oat phenols, the effect was to greatly improve the prevention of arteriosclerosis. So if you were to cut up an orange to eat with your oats, or drink a glass of pure orange juice with your oatmeal, you'd be doing yourself almost twice as much good.

BENEFITS FOR POST MENOPAUSAL WOMEN

Eating a portion of whole grains such as oats has been found to be especially good for women who have reached the menopause. At least six portions per week are apparently a good idea for treating high blood pressure, high cholesterol or other cardio vascular diseases. One study in Denmark found that women eating the most whole grains, nuts, seeds and berries had higher levels of lignan in their blood, which protects against breast and other hormone-dependent cancers and heart disease. Other studies have also highlighted an increase in sexual pleasure after eating more oats.

RESPONDING TO INFECTIONS

The beta-glucan found in oats helps the body's immune system to fight bacterial infection by helping to locate infected tissue rapidly. This rapid response results in faster clearance of micro-organisms and healing. Again, a bowl of porridge a day will boost your immune system.

ANTIOXIDANTS AND ANTI-CANCER TREATMENT

As well as being high in fibre, oats are a very good source of selenium, which works with vitamin E in a number of antioxidant systems throughout the body. Selenium also helps decrease asthma symptoms and heart disease and is associated with a reduced risk of colon cancer and other carcinogens in the gastrointestinal tract. Recent research has found that the benefits from whole grains like oats have been underestimated for a long time. Alongside corn, whole wheat and brown rice, oats provide high levels of phenolics, which are powerful antioxidants.

REGULAR HABITS
Insoluble fibres serve as effective laxatives and are thus useful in treating constipation. They have been used in treating diseases of the gall bladder and kidneys and in preventing diarrhoea.

ALTERNATIVE TO WHEAT FOR CELIAC DISEASE
Although celiac disease requires lifelong avoidance of gluten, which is found in wheat, rye, barley and oats, some adult sufferers have shown that oats are tolerated because they contain only a small amount of gluten. Children treated on a wheat-free diet with some oats for a year were shown to have improved lining of the small bowel, which is damaged by eating wheat gluten. Their immune systems had returned to normal.

MANY CLAIMS TO FAME
People suffering from rheumatism have found relief by eating porridge, as have those suffering from a hangover. Among the other benefits claimed for porridge are tackling obesity and aiding pregnancy. They are said to have aphrodisiac properties and are also reputed to regulate thyroid problems.

Oats are included in old remedies for nervous conditions, anxiety and insomnia and they alleviate water retention. Allegedly, eating oats can also help to deal with withdrawal symptoms from giving up smoking tobacco.

SKIN CONDITIONS
The medicinal qualities of oats derive from all parts of the plant, including the straw, green stems and leaves. Additionally, flours, soups, soaps, oat milk and other preparations can be made from them (see the section on beauty treatments).

Oats have often been used in baths to help skin conditions, have helped burns to heal and can reduce the effects of eczema. (NB. Although generally used as a useful compound in skin care, oats can also trigger skin problems in some people, so always test a small area of skin first). Being rich in silica, oats are also known to help renew bones, skin, nails, hair and other tissue.

FATIGUE

Oats are considered to be a very nourishing food to aid recovery from illness or exhaustion. The grains contain sterols and alkaloids which have been found to be beneficial in the reduction of anxiety. Oats have a relaxing and calming effect and are a rich source of iron, manganese and zinc. It's always surprising to see people put a bowl of porridge on their list of comfort foods, although I do agree that hot porridge in the morning gives a feeling of wellbeing. I can't see myself creeping down to make a quick fix of porridge at other times of the day, however. There must be some chemistry I'm missing. Claims have also been made for its long term effects against nervous illnesses, shingles, herpes and chronic depression.

INSOMNIA

Oat preparations contribute to the good functioning of the thyroid gland and of the entire endocrine system. Similar effects can be produced by mattresses and pillows filled with straw, chaff and oat leaves. A French friend vividly remembers his family being given mattresses filled with oat husks and straw when younger. He recalls sinking into these mattresses and falling asleep, aware of the popping of husks as he drifted off. The down side became apparent when he awoke — he couldn't turn over because he was moulded into the mattress, which then itched as the straw came through the covering. I think I'll pass on the mattress idea, but who knows what the oats could do, hidden in a well padded pillow?

FERTILITY

From Anglo Saxon times oats have been considered an important contribution to the health and fertility of women. Oats were one of five plants that were considered to restore a woman's fertility, the other plants being ginger, wheat, rose and cress.

It's not only humans who have claimed improvements in fertility and virility from eating oats. Read any farming or livestock journal and you will find advice about improving a bull's condition by extra oats in his diet before allowing him to visit his herd, or, less poetically, before the AI collector calls for the samples. That reminds me of the 'Rent-a-bull' adverts we used to read weekly in our local paper in North Yorkshire.

Horses also receive extra attention on the oats front when stamina is needed. Getting their oats, indeed!

APHRODISIAC QUALITIES

Research has apparently shown that oats have positive effects in reversing or combating not only sterility but also impotence. It is known that oat preparations contribute to the equilibrium of the endocrine and other systems and wild green oats are said to boost the effects of other herbal aphrodisiacs. Oats provide a stimulating effect on the body, and are said to free up bound testosterone, hence the term 'feeling his oats.' They are certainly considered to be good as a restorative tonic, ideal for energy deficiency. I read somewhere that wearing a kilt has quite an effect on male fertility and virility, so perhaps a bowl of oats just adds to the effect!

WORDS OF CAUTION

OATS AND PURINES

Oats contain naturally-occurring substances called purines, which are commonly found in plants, animals, and humans. In some individuals, excessive intake of these substances can cause health problems. Purines can be broken down to form uric acid, and too much of this can increase the risks related to kidney problems or gout. Sufferers of these conditions may want to limit or avoid foods such as oats.

Literary and Cultural Connections

Oats and oat based foods have given rise to a whole vocabulary that originated in Scotland but gradually spread far and wide. First of all, the generic term 'blanter' was used to describe food made from oats, for example oat bread and porridge. You could take a drink of 'blenshaw' with it, if you wished, a concoction of oatmeal, sugar, milk, water and nutmeg. If you came from North Roxburgh and you wanted to serve milk with your porridge, you would use your 'luggie', a small wooden bowl with handles formed from projecting staves.

'Brose' is a dish of oat- or pease-meal mixed with boiling water or milk, with salt and butter added, but you'd probably want to avoid it cooling so much that it left you with a 'brat', the crust or coating that forms on the surface of a liquid, such as curdled cream on milk or skin on your porridge. For the strong of stomach, especially in North Perth, a good dose of 'cauld steer(ie)', that is cold 'brose' — oatmeal stirred in cold water or sour milk — would set you up for the day, though, personally, I much prefer the sound of 'crackins', a dish of fried oatmeal, now found in the north-east.

Talking of the north-east, my husband's father, a coalminer from Sunderland who moved to Kent in the 1920s to find work in the newly opened collieries, always talked of the food he took with him to work as his 'snap' (kept securely in a miner's 'snap tin'). This was clearly a reference to 'snap and rattle' or toasted oatcakes crumbled in milk, famous in the north-east.

ANOTHER COUNTRY, ANOTHER NAME
Porridge itself — or the name for it — varies widely even within the confines of Scotland. For instance, the Gaelic word for it is 'lite' (pronounced leetch-yuh). In Shetland they use the word 'milgruel', and the thin porridge made with the liquor in which kale has been cooked is known as 'tartan-purry'. 'Brochan', a thick or thin gruel with, for example, butter and/or honey added, is sometimes considered to be a porridge, especially in Arygll and Ulster.

Rabbie Burns may well have described porridge as 'chief of Scotia's food' in his poem *The Cotter's Saturday Night*

(1786) but its fame and influence have certainly spread well beyond the boundaries of Scotland. The sheer number of different names for porridge dishes tells us what a significant part it plays in the life and culture of nations all around the world. In some countries it has medicinal qualities, helping patients to recuperate. For example, 'rice congee', a type of rice porridge eaten in several Asian countries, especially China, is valued for its therapeutic properties. It is also served in Japan, where it is known as 'kanji'.

Another Japanese porridge dish, called 'okayu', is given to sick people much in the way that chicken noodle soup is offered to ailing citizens in the USA. It is also commonly used by the Japanese to wean their infants onto solid foods. The fact that 'congee' is often served during times of famine underscores its importance as a staple to eke out meagre food supplies and puts us in mind of the place of porridge in the poorhouse, in the hard times of Dickensian England.

The porridge we all know and love in the UK, including 'flummery' (Wales) and 'fuarag' or 'crowdie' (Scotland), is called 'oatmeal' or 'oatmeal mush' in the United States. It is also a traditional Scandinavian and Icelandic breakfast. In Finland there is a porridge based Christmas food, eaten with cinnamon and sugar, known as 'ruishiutaleita'. In Norway, they have 'risgrøt', made with rice and vanilla, cooked with milk and served with cinnamon, sugar and butter, while in Morocco you may come across 'zematur'.

There are several types of maize porridge, such as grits, traditional in the southern United States. In Mexico, 'atole' is a warm, porridge-like concoction made with water and milk. In Romania 'mamaliga' is popular, as is 'cornmeal mush' in southern and mid-Atlantic US states.

In Italy 'polentina', which can be made from corn or barley, also contains raisins, milk and sugar. In southern India the traditional 'uppama' or 'uppma', a fried semolina ('suzi' or 'shuji') porridge, is flavoured with clarified butter, fried onions, toasted mustard seeds and curry leaves. It is also often mixed with vegetables and potatoes, fried red chillies, fried cauliflower and toasted peanuts or cashew nuts.

FOOD FOR THOUGHT
So many varieties of both names and dishes, and we haven't even mentioned 'peasemeal' (or 'pease'/'pea') porridge, buckwheat porridge mixed with yoghurt, popular in Russian ethnic areas and in the Caucasus region or 'quinoa' porridge (ground quinoa flakes mixed with cocoa or cinnamon) from ancient Mayan culture. Not to mention millet porridge, much favoured in the Middle East and often seasoned with cumin and honey, and, last but not least, rye porridge. No wonder Spike Milligan felt moved to campaign for a permanent reminder to us all of its enduring status, in his poem simply entitled 'Porridge'.

Ian Dury and the Blockheads also considered porridge to be one of their 'Reasons to be Cheerful', but their view was not shared by other creative artists. Despite the enthusiasm of Messrs Milligan and Dury, porridge has not always been a cause for celebration. Dr Johnson, in the first comprehensive English dictionary published in 1747, sarcastically dismissed oats as:

'a grain, which in England is generally given to horses, but in Scotland appears to support the people.'

Fortunately, the entry did not go unchallenged, since John Boswell, a writer from north of the border with England, offered the following, trenchant riposte:

'Which is why England is known for its horses and Scotland for its men.'

WHAT THE DICKENS . . . ?

Charles Dickens's alternative term for porridge — 'gruel' — could hardly be more fitting, given the circumstances to which his characters inevitably find themselves reduced. Impoverished, without friends and family and shamelessly exploited by an appallingly cruel society, they find themselves feeling so hungry they long for extra helpings of the most disgustingly unappetising food imaginable: a bowl of porridge.

> *Into these bowls, Mrs Squeers, assisted by the hungry servant, poured a brown composition, which looked like diluted pincushions without the covers, and was called porridge. A minute wedge of brown bread was inserted in each bowl, and when they had eaten their porridge by means of the bread, the boys ate the bread itself, and had finished their breakfast; whereupon Mr Squeers said, in a solemn voice, 'For what we have received, may the Lord make us truly thankful!' — and went away to his own.*

> (*Nicholas Nickelby* at Dotheboys Hall, following brimstone and treacle 'physiking' of new pupils).

Even when Nicholas enjoys slightly improved fortune, he still gorges himself on the stuff simply to fend off starvation:

> *Nicholas distended his stomach with a bowl of porridge, for much the same reason which induces some savages to swallow earth — lest they should be inconveniently hungry when there is nothing to eat. Having further disposed of a slice of bread and butter, allotted to him in virtue of his office, he sat himself down, to wait for school-time.*

'PLEASE SIR, I WANT SOME MORE, SIR.'

In *Oliver Twist*, porridge — or the relative lack of it —
threatens to become the cause of even murder and
cannibalism, leading to one of the most famous literary
moments of all time:

> The room in which the boys were fed, was a large stone
> hall, with a copper at one end: out of which the master,
> dressed in an apron for the purpose, and assisted by one
> or two women, ladled the gruel at meal-times. Of this
> festive composition each boy had one porringer, and no
> more — except on occasions of great public rejoicing,
> when he had two ounces and a quarter of bread besides.
> The bowls never wanted washing. The boys polished them
> with their spoons till they shone again; and when they
> had performed this operation (which never took very long,
> the spoons being nearly as large as the bowls), they would
> sit staring at the copper, with such eager eyes, as if they
> could have devoured the very bricks of which it was
> composed; employing themselves, meanwhile, in sucking
> their fingers most assiduously, with the view of catching
> up any stray splashes of gruel that might have been cast
> thereon. Boys have generally excellent appetites. Oliver
> Twist and his companions suffered the tortures of slow
> starvation for three months: at last they got so voracious
> and wild with hunger, that one boy, who was tall for his
> age, and hadn't been used to that sort of thing (for his
> father had kept a small cook-shop), hinted darkly to his
> companions, that unless he had another basin of gruel
> per diem, he was afraid he might some night happen to eat
> the boy who slept next him, who happened to be a weakly
> youth of tender age. He had a wild, hungry eye; and they
> implicitly believed him. A council was held;
> lots were cast who should walk up to the master after
> supper that evening, and ask for more; and it fell to
> Oliver Twist.

THE BARD AND THE BOWL

Shakespeare was no stranger to the attributes of porridge and made reference to it throughout his works. In *Macbeth* Banquo uses it as a potent symbol of personal matters, in which, he claims, he would never dream of meddling, declaring: 'I never thrust my nose in other men's porridge.' The cynical, sarcastic Sebastian, in *The Tempest*, uses the term to conjure up an admittedly repellent image ('cold porridge') with which he mocks Alonso, who is trying to be positive about their misfortune in being stranded on a remote island following the shipwreck:

> ALONSO: *Prithee, peace.*
> SEBASTIAN: *[Apart to Antonio] He receives*
>   *comfort like cold porridge.*

Since porridge could also be made from peas ('peace') Sebastian no doubt thought his pun about porridge was both clever and witty. In *The Tragedy of King Lear*, Edgar, posing as Tom, a demented beggar (the name 'Tom' was common amongst beggars at the time) tells Lear of his supposed woes and enemies, and how his own particular demon (the 'foul fiend') has tormented him, even trying to poison his porridge:

> KING LEAR
> *Didst thou give all to thy two daughters?*
> *And art thou come to this?*
>
> EDGAR
> *Who gives any thing to poor Tom? whom the foul*
> *fiend hath led through fire and through flame, and*
> *through sword and whirlpool o'er bog and quagmire;*
> *that hath laid knives under his pillow, and halters*
> *in his pew; set ratsbane by his porridge;*

ONE MAN'S PORRIDGE . . .

Ironically, Jean-Jacques Rousseau (1712—1778), a French philosopher and writer, who believed in the natural goodness of man (whom he felt was warped by society) and whose work influenced the theories of the French Revolution and the Romantics, felt his enemies kept trying to poison his porridge when he visited Scotland. He also deserves credit for his promotion of vegetarianism, thanks to his support for natural foods, including porridge. As he said in *Emile*:

> *'One of the proofs that the taste of flesh is not natural to man is the indifference which children exhibit for that sort of meat, and the preference they all give to vegetable foods, such as milk-porridge, pastry, fruits, etc.'*

Some people, of course, need no persuading that porridge on its own (and, no doubt, Scottish cuisine, for those wanting to show their hatred of all things Scottish) is poison enough: for Ronnie Barker, in the richly comic series of the same name, porridge — also known, with obvious connections, as 'stir' — was something imposed on you, in this case a stretch in prison. Scots should feel free to dismiss this as mere culinary racism on the part of the English or 'sassenachs' (an ancient derogatory term for a Saxon), who should know better, as was clearly the case with Cosmo Gordon Lang, Archbishop of Canterbury from 1928 to 1942; he once infamously remarked to his audience in Edinburgh: 'If you take the shorter catechism, the psalms, and Sir Walter Scott, and mix them with porridge, you will breed a great race of men.'

STAND UP FOR PORRIDGE!

Porridge is the subject of numerous superstitions and legends. Talking of 'stir', there are those who insist that porridge should be stirred in a clockwise direction using the right hand, to avoid invoking the devil. This stirring should be done with a straight wooden spoon without a moulded or flat end, known as a 'spurtle' or 'theevil' (see page 68). Curiously, you should also always refer to porridge as 'they' and, according to custom, you should eat it with a bone spoon whilst standing up.

Quite recently, HM Prisons finally decided to stop offering porridge to inmates for breakfast; as an economy measure, they have replaced it with individual boxes of cereal and a third of a pint of milk, placed inside prisoners' cells before the previous night's lock-up. Although porridge is clearly not as popular as it was in prisons, there are surely still some who rue the passing of the institution — the homely, warming comfort of an early morning bowl. For old lags it is even more serious than that; according to one of their superstitions, on the day of their release from prison, they should eat a large bowl of porridge — if they fail to finish it off, the story goes, they will inevitably be forced to return to prison to finish it, while they are doing another stretch!

A (MING) VASE FULL OF PORRIDGE?

According to legend, Zhu Yuanzhang, a man of lowly birth who became the first emperor of the Ming Dynasty (1368–1644), was the founding father of the '8th December Porridge Festival'. Allegedly, on December 8th the young Zhu and some of his hungry friends cooked up a porridge from some rice, corn and beans they had found stored for winter in a mousehole in a field. Years later Zhu led his poor people in the uprising that overthrew the emperor and saw Zhu installed in his place. The banquet of coarse cereal porridge he held on December 8th each year, to remind him of his humble origins and of the time when he had tasted the most delicious food ever, gave rise to today's '8th December Porridge Festival' of Tianjin, a city that once served as a stronghold for Beijing.

THE WORD ACCORDING TO MACGONAGAL

Another of Scotland's poets, William MacGonagal (1830–1902), the most awful rhymester to have walked the Highlands, took great inspiration from his oatmeal breakfast, particularly on his travels.

> 'So of course I went in and got a good breakfast of porridge and good Highland milk, enough to make a hungry soul to sing with joy, especially in a strange country, and far from home. Well, having breakfasted, I arose and bade the servant girl good-bye, at the same time thanking her and the shepherd — her master — for their kindness towards me.'

Perhaps we should not blame porridge for the fact that he went on to pen immortal and (unintentionally) excruciatingly funny lines such as those below, giving rise to countless MacGonagal societies devoted to public readings.

> 'The chains of mountains there is most frightful to see,
> Along each side of the Spittal o' Glenshee;
> But the Castleton o' Braemar is most beautiful to see,
> With its handsome whitewashed houses,
> and romantic scenery,
> And bleak-looking mountains, capped with snow,
> Where the deer and the roe do ramble to and fro,
> Near by the dark river Dee,
> Which is most beautiful to see.'

A STITCH IN TIME?

The metaphor that most readily springs to mind in connection with oats is, of course, 'sowing one's wild oats'. But what are the origins of the expression? The wild oat, a common tall plant that looks like the cereal plant oat, is, in fact, a weed that is difficult to root out. Hence the expression to 'sow wild oats' means to behave improperly, like sowing weeds instead of productive grain. There is an element of ageism in the expression, as it is always applied to young people, who are usually accused of indulging in prolific sexual adventures. In the 16th and 17th century dissolute or wild young men were called 'wild oats." If we remember that oats scatter and shatter as soon as they ripen, making them difficult to harvest, and that oats are supposed to have aphrodisiac qualities, it's not difficult to see the connection between oats and unbridled sexual passion (or, as John Lennon humorously puts it on 'Abbey Road', in a spoken link between tracks: 'Phase one, in which Doris gets her oats!').

SING FOR YOUR BREAKFAST

Finally, porridge deservedly has its place in the world of music, including the name of a famous band performing Celtic music to modern arrangements: *The Porridgemen*. Perhaps the final lyric should go to the wonderfully onomatopoeic 'Sink Song'. Altogether now:

Scouring out the porridge pot
Round and round and round

Out with all the scraith and scoopery
Lift the eely ooly droopery
Chase the glubbery slubbery gloopery
Round and round and round

Out with all the doleful dithery
Ladle out the slimey slithery
Hunt and catch the hithery thithery
Round and round and round.

Out with all the ubbly gubbly
On the stove it burns so bubbly
Use a spoon and use it doubly
Round and round and round.

Beauty
Treatments
With Oats

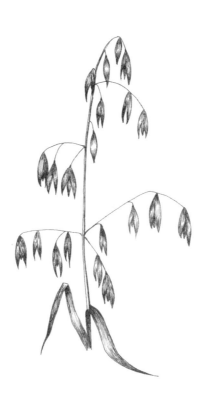

The following recipes can mostly be made from basic ingredients that you probably already have in the kitchen, so even if you can't afford to treat yourself to a pricey product, you can enjoy a bit of pampering. I've included some more adventurous recipes for interest.

CAUTION

If you have sensitive skin, or are liable to be sensitive to some products, be careful and test on a small area first. Sensitive skins should be especially careful with lemon juice and avocado.

Also be aware that oats can block drains, along with clay, oil or honey, so do the environmentally friendly thing, and remove face packs and cleansers over a bin instead of down the sink.

BEAUTY TREATMENT RECIPES

OATMEAL FACE MASK

This is a very simple face mask that you can make quickly and cheaply. If you don't use it straight away, refrigerate to keep it fresh. It is best to make just before use.

You will need:
 2 tablespoons uncooked porridge oats
 1 to 2 tablespoons plain yoghurt

Method:
1. Combine the oats and 1 tablespoon of the yoghurt, stirring the oatflakes up so that they begin to break apart. Stir to a creamy consistency, adding more yoghurt if necessary.
2. Spread the mixture over your face and neck, avoiding the eyes. Relax for several minutes — maybe in the bath.
3. When the mask has dried rinse gently with warm water.

OATMEAL AND HONEY CLEANSER

This is another recipe made entirely from ingredients from the store cupboard. The decision of whether to use olive oil or vinegar for mixing is up to you and your skin type. Olive oil is best for normal to dry skin and vinegar if your skin errs on the greasy side. Don't use malt vinegar, however, which is chemically produced and won't smell nice, apart from possibly making your skin smart. Cider vinegar or any mild fruit vinegar would be best. You don't need much, anyway. It will keep for up to three months, so you could increase the proportions, but I think it is best to make just enough for one application.

You will need:
 1 tablespoon finely ground oats
 1 tablespoon wheat bran
 1 tablespoon honey
 Olive oil or cider vinegar to form a paste

Method:
1. Mix the oatmeal, wheat bran and honey together in a bowl. Add enough olive oil or cider vinegar to form a paste.
2. Rinse your face with warm water, apply the cleanser and massage it gently into the skin.
3. Rinse with warm water then splash your face with cold water.

SIMPLE OATMEAL AND HONEY CLEANSER

This simple mask takes advantage of the cleansing and softening properties of oats and the hydrating properties of honey.

You will need:
> 3 tablespoons oatmeal
> 2 tablespoons clear honey

Method:
1. Put the two ingredients in a bowl and stir well. The mixture will be quite stiff.
2. Apply to a clean face and relax for about 15 minutes.
3. Rinse well with warm water, depositing the oats in a bin.

OATMEAL CLEANSER FOR SENSITIVE SKIN

You will need:
> 250ml (fluid oz) warm water
> 120g (4 oz) oatmeal
> 1 tablespooon glycerine or honey

Method:
1. Put all of the ingredients into a blender bowl and process until smooth.
2. Place a little of the mixture on your palms and gently massage into your skin.
3. Rinse with more warm water and pat dry.

CINNAMON OATMEAL MILK BATH

If you can bear to part with it, this also makes a wonderful home-made gift idea. This is enough for 4—5 baths and can be stored in a jar or decorative container.

You will need:
>   120g (4 oz) cornstarch
>   225g (8 oz) powdered milk
>   60g (2 oz) medium oatmeal
> $^1/_2$ teaspoon cinnamon

Method:
1. Mix all ingredients in blender or food processor until you have a fine powder.
2. Add about 2 tablespoons of the mixture to your bathwater for a soothing bath.

DEEP FACIAL HONEY & OATMEAL CLEANSER

Honey is a natural antibiotic and is extremely nourishing.

You will need for 1 mask:
>   1 tablespoon honey
>   1 tablespoon oatmeal
>   2 slices cucumber

Method:
1. Mix the honey and oatmeal together till thick. Adjust the proportions if necessary.
2. Apply as a face-pack and place the cucumber on your eyes.
3. Rest for half an hour then wash off.

CUCUMBER FACE MASK FOR SENSITIVE SKIN

You will need:

$1/4$ large cucumber, peeled and seeded

1 tablespoon whipping cream

$1/2$ tablespoon clear honey

About 8 teaspoons finely powdered oats

Method:

1. Place the peeled and seeded cucumber in a blender and process until liquefied.

2. Add the whipping cream and honey and process until smooth.

3. Add the oats and process further until a paste-like mixture is formed. Add more oats if the cucumber was very watery.

4. Smooth a thick layer over clean skin and rest for 15 minutes. Rinse with warm water and apply moisturiser.

OATMEAL BATH SOAK

This is good for a dry, itchy skin.

The use of an old stocking or pair of tights makes the recipe less messy and easier to manage.

You will need:

2 to 3 cups porridge oatflakes (not instant)

3 tablespoons olive oil

5 drops essential oil of your choice, or make unscented

You also need a pair of old tights or a stocking.

Method:

1. If you use essential oils, combine these for an hour or two with the olive oil before starting.

2. Mix in the oats until they are coated with the oils.

3. Pour into the old tights and tie up securely.

4. Add to a warm bath and soak yourself for at least 20 minutes.

Dispose of the bag immediately after use.

OIL FREE OATMEAL BATH SOAK

You will need:

    120g oatmeal
    120g cornstarch
    You also need a pair of old tights or a stocking.

Method:
As previous recipe (Oatmeal Bath Soak see page 53). I think the use of the old tights will save a lot of cleaning of plug holes!

BANANA BALM

This is a cleanser and moisturiser in one and suits all skin types, especially dry. The essential oil is optional.

You will need:

    $^1/_2$ fresh banana
    1 tablespoon fresh whipping cream, lightly warmed
    1 teaspoon honey, slightly warmed
    Approximately 1 tablespoon fine oatmeal
    Few drops essential oil

Method:
1. Mash the banana to a creamy pulp.
2. Warm the honey and whipping cream in a microwave for about 15 seconds.
3. Stir well, then add to the banana pulp.
4. Add the oats and essential oil (optional) and stir again.
5. To use, massage over dampened skin using gentle, sweeping, upward motions.
6. Rinse well and follow with a toner and moisturiser.

LEMON-GINGER OATMEAL FACIAL

The essential oils are cleansing and astringent while the oats are soothing and gentle.

You will need:
> 2 tablespoons ground oats
> 1 tablespoon buttermilk or skimmed milk
> 1 egg white
> 1 drop ginger essential oil
> 1 drop lemon essential oil

Method:
1. Combine the buttermilk or skimmed milk and egg white. Stir vigorously.
2. Add to the oats and stir until a smooth paste forms. If the mixture is too runny, add a few more oats to absorb some of the liquid.
3. Add the essential oils and stir.
4. Smooth a layer of the mask over your clean face and neck, avoiding the eyes. Rest for 10—15 minutes.
5. Rinse well with warm water and pat face and neck dry. Follow with toner and moisturiser.

YOGHURT, OATMEAL AND TOMATO FACIAL

You will need:
> $1/4$ of a tomato, skinned, mashed and deseeded
> 3 teaspoons plain yoghurt
> 1 teaspoon mashed cucumber
> 1 teaspoon aloe gel
> 3 teaspoons oatmeal
> 2 mint leaves (crushed)

Method:
1. Put the ingredients together in a blender, or mash and sieve.
2. Apply to your face and leave for about 10 minutes.
3. Rinse with warm water.

APPLE, CUCUMBER AND OATMEAL PICK-ME-UP

You will need:

1 cup oatmeal, ground finely
an apple, peeled and cored
5 cm (2 in.) of a cucumber, peeled
2 tablespoons milk

Method:
1. Cut the apple and cucumber up before putting into a blender with the rest of the ingredients.
2. Apply to the face and leave on for 20 minutes. Wash off with lukewarm water. This mask may help to reduce redness, oil and blackheads.

MAPLE OAT FACIAL SCRUB

Maple syrup has a sweet and nectar-like aroma that blends nicely with lots of essential oils, plus its texture makes it a surprisingly effective medium for a soothing facial scrub. Besides, if you can't eat the stuff, how else will you use up that special gift from a relative's Canadian holiday?

You will need:

3 tablespoons finely powdered oats
1 tablespoon pure maple syrup
1 tablespoon milk
2 drops lemon essential oil (optional)
1 drop sweet orange essential oil (optional)

Method:
1. Warm the milk in a microwave for about 15 seconds.
2. Combine the maple syrup and milk and stir well.
3. Add oats and stir. Let them rest for 5 minutes.
4. Add essential oils and stir again to ensure the mix.
5. Tie back long hair and wet the face and scoop the mixture into your palms. Apply to face and neck using upward, sweeping motions, and gentle, circular motions to clean the skin.
6. Rinse well and follow with toner and moisturiser.

PUMPKIN FACE MASK

Pumpkins are full of beta-carotene and vitamin A, making it especially nourishing for your skin. This sounds an ideal recipe to try at Halloween time. You might not even need a mask!

You will need:

> 1 miniature pumpkin, or portion of a larger one
> 4 pineapple chunks
> 1 tablespoon finely powdered oats
> 1 tablespoon finely powdered almonds
> 1 teaspoon milk
> 1 teaspoon honey
> 1 teaspoon olive oil
> 2 drops rose geranium essential oil

Method:

1. Use a sharp knife to core the pumpkin and slice on a cutting board. Cut about 6-8 pieces.
2. Place pumpkin pieces (including seeds) in a microwave safe dish with about $1/4$ cup of water. Microwave for about 2 minutes until the flesh is soft. Allow to cool. Cut the peel off.
3. Place pumpkin flesh, seeds and strings into a small food processor with the pineapple and blend until smooth.
4. Add oats, almonds, milk and honey in that order, processing after each addition. Add the oil and stir.
5. Add essential oils. The texture should be rich and smooth, with just a slight graininess from the almonds.
6. To use, apply a layer to clean and tone face and neck skin. Rest for 15 minutes. Rinse well with warm water and follow with moisturiser.

ALMOND OAT CLEANSER

This mix of natural ingredients is easy to make ahead of time. It is a very soothing mask for sensitive skin. Refrigerate before using as the cool sensation of the product is mildly stimulating.

You will need:

1 tablespoon brewer's yeast
1 tablespoon fine oatmeal
$^1/_2$ cucumber
2 tablespoons plain yoghurt
1 teaspoon honey

Method:
1. Mix together the yeast and oats in a small bowl and set aside.
2. Peel and slice the cucumber and blend until no chunks remain. Add the yoghurt and honey and mix again.
3. Add the brewer's yeast and oats to the mixture and process to combine.
4. Apply to a clean face and neck skin and leave on for 15—30 minutes.
5. Rinse well and follow with toner and moisturiser.

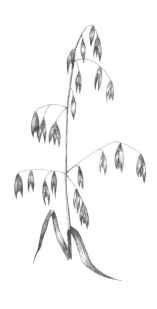

These recipes require slightly more planning, unless you have special clay or fuller's earth lying around. The clays and soap bases are available by mail order via the internet from various suppliers. A vegetable-based melt and poursoap base, makes clear soap bars with good foaming and moisturising qualities. The soap has a pH value of 7.5-8 before the addition of essential oils.

AVOCADO AND CUCUMBER FACEMASK

You will need:

$^1/_4$ of a cucumber, peeled and chopped
an avocado
3 tablespoons finely powdered oats
3 tablespoons of water
1 tablespoon fresh lemon juice
1 teaspoon honey
8-9 tablespoons green clay or kaolin
Few drops of essential oils (optional)

Method:
1. Puree the cucumber and avocado flesh in a food processor with water and lemon juice until smooth.
2. Add the oats, honey and essential oils.
3. Pour the mix into a bowl and then whisk in the clay. Apply to clean face and neck and leave on for 20–30 minutes.
4. Rinse off with warm water then use a toner and moisturiser.

GENTLE MILK & OATMEAL FACIAL

You will need:

2 tablespoons pink kaolin clay
1 tablespoon fine oatmeal
1 teaspoon buttermilk powder
1 teaspoon rose hips seed oil
Enough lavender water to make a thick paste

Method:

1. Combine the dry ingredients in a bowl.
2. Add the lavender water a little at a time until the mixture turns into a paste.
3. Apply to the skin in a gentle circular motion, and leave it for about 10–20 minutes, but don't let the clay dry out.
4. Wash off with warm water.

HERBAL OATMEAL SOAP

This herbal, aromatic and soothing soap is great for dry skin. The recipe will make several bars. You can add or change the herbs and dried flowers to suit your preferences.

You will need:

500g (1lb) soap base
$1/4$ teaspoon rosemary essential oil
$1/4$ teaspoon sage essential oil
$1/4$ teaspoon lavender essential oil
1 cup oatmeal
$1/4$ cup dried chamomile flowers
$1/4$ cup calendula petals
$1/8$ cup marsh mallow root
$1/8$ cup dried nettle
$1/8$ cup dried rosemary
$1/8$ cup dried rose hips
$1–1^1/2$ cups distilled water

Method:

1. A few hours before making this soap, combine the water, oatmeal and herbs in a saucepan.

2. Heat to boiling, then cover and simmer for at least 30 minutes. Cool, preferably covered.

3. Strain it through a double or triple muslin cloth or pair of tights, saving the liquid. Throw away the oatmeal and herbs.

4. Cut the soap base into small cubes and place in a microwave safe measuring cup/bowl. Either microwave on high setting for 30 seconds at a time, stirring in-between until the base is nearly melted, or melt the soap in a container in a pan of water on the cooker.

5. Stir the base slowly to avoid air bubbles. Your now-liquid base will be very hot. Let it cool down until you can comfortably touch it, stirring slowly.

6. Add the herbal slurry and essential oils. Stir gently and pour into moulds or small clean containers that you can get the soap out of when set.

The bars can be used as soon as they are completely hardened. Use for face and body in bath or shower.

CREAMY OATMEAL SOAP

You will need:

> 500g (1 lb) soap base
> 1 teaspoon milk & honey fragrance oil
> $^1/_4$ cup oatmeal

Method:

1. Melt the soap in a microwave or double boiler until fully melted. Do not let it get too hot.

2. Allow the soap to cool slightly until it forms a thin skin on the top.

3. Quickly add fragrance and stir slightly. Don't stir too much as this will cause air bubbles to form and the soap will cool too fast.

4. When the soap starts to thicken to a porridge consistency, add the oats and stir gently. If the soap is too runny, all the oats will end up on one side.

5. Pour into moulds or small containers.

HEMP SEED FACE POLISH
WITH GREEN TEA (FOR MEN)

The hemp seed flour contributes a smooth exfoliating texture with the benefits of essential fatty acids. Green Tea is a good antioxidant and oat flour a soothing cleanser. Chick pea flour can be used instead of hemp seed flour, for convenience.

You will need:

> 1 cup oat flour
> $^1/_4$ cup hemp seed flour (or chick pea flour)
> 2 green tea bags
> 15 drops lime essential oil
> 5 drops cypress essential oil
> 5 drops lavender essential oil
> 5 drops juniper berry essential oil

Method:

1. Place the oat flour and hemp seed flour in a clean bowl and mix. Break open the green tea bags and add the tea to the flours and mix well.
2. Add the essential oils, one by one, stirring after each.
3. Transfer to a clean air-tight container. Leave the mixture for 3—5 days before using.
4. Use a clean spoon to scoop about a quarter of the mixture into the palm of your hand. Mix with enough water, herbal tea or hydrosol to make a smooth paste.
5. Massage gently over face and neck. Rinse well.

Fascinating Facts

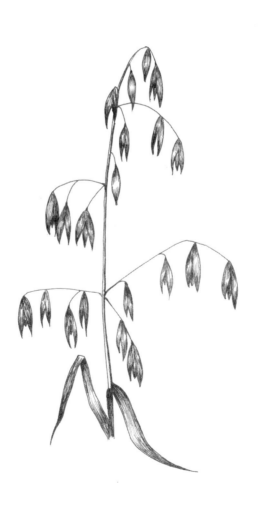

DID YOU KNOW . . . ?

NORSE NOUS

In the age of the Vikings porridge was not only cooked to provide nourishment for hungry explorers, marauders and pillagers. The metalwork of their cooking utensils, in particular their cooking pots, often left gaps through which food, liquids and, of course, valuable heat could be lost during cooking. Therefore, the canny Vikings worked out a cunning plan to seal their pots, for more efficient and economical mealtimes.

They cooked up either fruit or porridge in the unsealed pot and allowed the boiling contents to ooze through the gapped metalwork. Once on the outside of the pot, the boiling fruit or porridge would soon burn and coat the outer surface, thus closing the offending breaches. All that then remained to be done was to clean the inside of the pot before cooking anything else in it. Yum, yum, Erik!

TOPPING UP THE POT

People in North America in the 1500s often cooked in the kitchen in a big kettle hung over the fire. Every day they lit the fire and added things to the pot to make a stew, consisting mainly of vegetables, as there wasn't a lot of meat to be had. Any leftovers would remain in the pot to go cold overnight and then be used to start a 'fresh' stew the following day – not the healthiest of diets, as the stew could end up having food in it that had been in there for a month. This doubtless gave rise to the chant: 'Peas porridge hot, peas porridge cold, peas porridge in the pot nine days old.'

THICK SKIN, THIN SKIN

The asphodel plant, like oats, is versatile, not only as a source of food but also for its medicinal applications. As far back as the 4th century, Theophrastus explained how the asphodel stem could be fried, the seed toasted and the root chopped and eaten with figs. When used to treat skin conditions, particularly those caused by over-exposure to sun or harsh weather, it eases irritation and softens and refreshes. Porridge made from fresh asphodel roots has also been used to lighten freckles.

THE PORRIDGE POT — CRATER MASS?

If you saw a photograph of the Porridge Pot — a swirling, bubbling, mud volcano in New Zealand — you'd understand immediately how it got its name. Since it is created by hot spring activity, with lots of sulphurous gas and small amounts of water reacting chemically with surrounding rock, you'd probably also be able to conjure up the appalling, acrid smell, too. Oats may well be associated with beauty care, but this particular porridge pot wouldn't guarantee you the finest of mud to apply as a face pack — unless you fancy a complexion like the surface of Mercury!

DEVIL'S PORRIDGE

The Devil's Porridge exhibition tells the story of HM Factory in Gretna, described as 'the greatest munitions factory on earth'. In 1915, Britain was losing the First World War, through acute lack of ammunition. The war effort was transformed by the arrival of 30,000 women and men from all over the world, who came to work in the massive munitions factory on the Solway, where cordite production rapidly outstripped that of all the other munitions factories in Britain combined.

Sir Arthur Conan Doyle, creator of the immortal detective, Sherlock Holmes, coined the term 'devil's porridge', when he visited the factory, in 1918. There he found the workers mixing by hand a curious, highly explosive paste, a mixture of nitro-glycerine and nitro-cotton. Once dried, the paste was processed into cordite, making it look like uncooked spaghetti. This potent concoction was then put into artillery shells and bullets to propel them, delivering quick, hot bursts of energy to the enemy.

PORRIDGE POT ALLEY

The name 'Porridge Pot' is highly popular — you will come across hundreds of restaurants and pubs within and beyond the British Isles bearing the name. There is even a road called 'Porridge Pot Alley' in London. I wonder if it's related to 'Tin Pan Alley'?

QUOTATIONS, PROVERBS AND SAYINGS

Esau sold his birthright for a bowl of the stuff, Cervantes advised his readers to keep their cool and mind their own porridge, Robert Browning was fascinated by the thought of John Keats's particular mix of porridge and George Eliot was convinced that sweet porridge was enough to bestow enviable calm and serenity on the face of a child. As for Noel Coward, he felt strongly that spoilt porridge was nothing short of calamitous. What do you read into their famous musings?

'Spare your breath to cool your porridge.'
'I never thrust my nose into other men's porridge.
It is no bread and butter of mine:
every man for himself and God for us all.'

Cervantes (1547—1616)

'Who fished the murex up?
What porridge had John Keats?'

Robert Browning (1812—1889)

'She was perfectly quiet now, but not asleep — only
soothed by sweet porridge and warmth into that wide-
gazing calm which makes us older human beings, with our
inward turmoil, feel a certain awe in the presence of a
little child, such as we feel before some quiet majesty or
beauty in the earth or sky — before a steady glowing
planet, or a full-flowered eglantine, or the bending trees
over a silent pathway.'

George Eliot (1819—1880)

'There's sand in the porridge and sand in the bed,
And if this is pleasure we'd rather be dead.'

Noel Coward (1899—1973)

Whatever conclusions you draw from these famous words, you will be sure to come across many bowls full of proverbs cooked up across the world, as in these three examples, drawn from Old England and the Russia of old:

> *'Crumb not your bread before you taste your porridge.'*
> (Old English saying: Think before you act)

> *'Porridge cannot be spoiled with butter.'*
> (Russian saying: If something is genuinely good and worthwhile, nothing can spoil it)

> *'As you cooked the porridge, so must you eat it.'*
> (Russian saying: Everyone must accept the consequences of his own actions)

THE GOLDEN SPURTLE

If you were to journey to Inverness-shire in October you might be in for a surprise. No, there wouldn't be a teddy bears' picnic to greet you, but Goldilocks herself would be hard pressed not to find a dish to her taste. Carrbridge is the venue for the World Porridge Making Championships, held in conjunction with the Highland Food and Drink Festival, or Highland Feast.

In recent years this has become more of an international event, with interest spreading across the globe. Connoisseurs travel to the event to compete for the coveted Golden Spurtle, along with other prizes. Recipes for the perfect porridge, along with a range of other ingredients, are tried and tested by judges in different categories.

The spurtle itself is a long-handled implement resembling on first inspection a thin rounders bat or truncheon. Spurtles have been in existence since at least the 16th century. There are two types: one spatula type for turning oatcakes and scones, the second a tapered stick for stirring porridge. A closer look obviously shows marked differences not apparent from an initial impression. Spurtles are also known as theevils or theedles in localised areas of Scotland. They were used before the introduction of rolled oats, when the oatmeal needed more time for softening and therefore required a longer cooking time. The use of a spurtle prevented the formation of large, stodgy lumps, like the sort I got when I first tried to cook medium oatmeal in a microwave, without frequently stirring it. That particular consignment went in the bin.

SPURTLE ETIQUETTE
Various traditions survive in some quarters, whereby the whole process of making successful porridge and consuming it rely on certain procedures and what could be described as old wives' tales. But who can be sure which is which? I'll let you decide.

Stirring 'widdershins' is said to invoke the devil or bring bad luck. You should always stir 'deiseal', that is sunwise or clockwise. Use of the left hand for stirring is equally bad news. This tradition obviously goes back to the days of witch hunts and the idea of left handed people being sinister (from the Latin 'sinister', meaning left). Interestingly, that would not have prevented my late, left handed mother-in-law from stirring the porridge in her native Scotland. She was forced as a child at school in Glasgow to use her right hand for writing and other tasks and became fairly competent with both, if not completely ambidextrous.

Addition of salt too early in the porridge-making process hardens the grain. This prevents swelling and results in a less creamy bowl of porridge. Ah well, on a low salt diet, I'll just have to put up with cooking it a bit longer, or settle for second best.

The traditional way of referring to porridge is 'they' and 'they' should be stirred with a spurtle, rather than a spoon.

Eat 'them' at the table, standing up. This possibly originates from when oats were eaten as whole grains, which must have weighed heavily on the stomach. Several accounts, ancient and modern, suggest that this tradition still survives.

Goldilocks & The National Literacy Strategy

I spent a large proportion of my teaching career as a primary school teacher. During the 1990s major changes took place within the prescribed curriculum with the introduction of the National Curriculum. This was later enhanced by other strategies, including the National Literacy Strategy, launched in 1997, which defined more specifically which areas of literature and language should be experienced by pupils in their various school years. Much of what I had to cover with a class of older pupils preparing for secondary school life and Standard Assessment Tasks at the end of Key Stage 2 (Year 6 being the last year at Primary School) was dreary beyond belief, especially the endless grammar niceties that children don't appreciate or even fully understand.

One of the highlights with Year 6 pupils who had, by then, generally developed a good sense of humour, was to identify key features of different types of writing; to identify stock characters, plot, structure and how particular texts conform, develop or undermine the type through for instance, parody. The children always enjoyed writing for a purpose and writing stories for younger pupils in the school. We experimented over the years, with the class working in groups to write and illustrate stories for Key Stage 1 (Infants), creating computer books using PowerPoint, using a digital camera to take mock-up scenes for further computer books, and so on.

Parody is something which children seem to pick up on faster these days than even 10 or 15 years ago. Discussing moral issues and presenting these issues in written form for others to understand is another important part of Literacy teaching, so obviously a story whereby a little girl wanders into a law-abiding house of bears, who live a quiet life and follow the healthy and active lifestyle which is much in the news at the moment (what with rising figures for child obesity and declining participation in sport, in favour of computer games and DVDs), always rankled. It always annoyed me that such a sweet little girl got away with such vandalism, theft and destruction and yet the bears were punished! Surely Goldilocks should have had several lessons in Citizenship, Personal, Social and Health Education, as well as talks from the local police liaison officer about personal safety. Maybe she should have been given an ASBO (Anti Social Behaviour Order) instead for her trouble.

When I was asked to write this book, I approached my old school, Hankham Primary School, near Pevensey in East Sussex. Mike Round, the Head Teacher, was very happy for me to visit and invite pupils to write their own version of Goldilocks, with the real purpose of inclusion in a real book. The best is included below. I think you'll agree that parody and humour are alive and well in Hankham.

GOLDILOCKS AND THE THREE BEARS

Once upon a time, there was a naughty little girl named Goldilocks. When I say naughty, I mean naughty. Anyway, her parents sent her off to the forest to look for some firewood as she was getting under their feet. She had collected quite a large pile when she suddenly saw a very peculiar sight. A girl, a lion, a Tin-man and a scarecrow were outside a pretty little cottage banging on the door.

'Hey you!' she called out.
'What are you doing? You aren't supposed to be in this story! Now be off with you!'

They hurried on and out of Goldilocks sight. As Goldilocks drew nearer she realised that the house was very odd and crooked. She left her basket and walked inside, without ever considering her actions.

The first thing she noticed were three bowls of hot and spicy porridge. Suddenly she felt very hungry. There was a big bowl, a medium bowl and a small bowl. Goldilocks tried the big bowl but it was much too hot and spicy. Then she tried the middle bowl but it was too sour. Then she tried the last bowl and it was just right; a flavour of chocolate trickled down her throat.

The next thing she noticed was three chairs. She was feeling tired after her long walk and needed a rest. There was a big one, a medium one and a tiny, weeny one. Goldilocks tried the big chair but it was too hard. Then she had a go on the middle chair but it was much too soft. Then she tried the smallest chair and it was just right! But then there was a snap, a crack and the chair completely broke and lay in a splintered mess on the floor. Panicking with the guilt of the incident, she ran upstairs to find herself in a pretty bedroom that had three beds all in a row.

She heard some loud snoring and the sheets moving up and down. She pulled back the cover to find a very hairy, huge and ugly wolf. In the next bed lay a very old granny. And in the smallest bed was Red Riding Hood:

'Hey, you three, you're not supposed to be in this story!' 'Oh, sorry about that', exclaimed Little Red Riding Hood and out they went, through the window, and out of Goldilocks sight.

She snuggled into the first bed but it was much too lumpy. The next bed was far too soft and feathery. But the last bed she tried was just right, and moments later she was fast asleep.

She was suddenly woken up with a loud BANG!
Three bears had returned and were very cross at the
mess in their house! So Goldilocks ran downstairs to
escape but found that in fact the baby bear was the
tallest of the three and the father bear was the shortest
of the three. The bears were so grateful to her for
chasing away the fairy tale burglars that they invited her
to stay for tea.

By Charlotte Reynard, aged 10 years
Hankham Primary School

Recipes

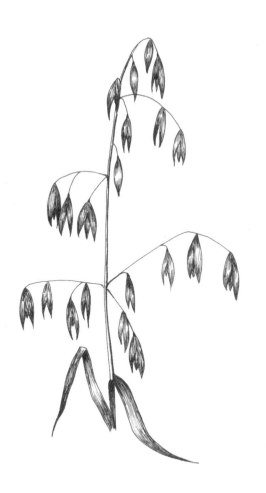

COOKING WITH OATS

Now that you're convinced that oats are an essential part of a balanced diet and really do you good, here are a few general uses and ways of sliding them into dishes for the non-porridge-eating members of the family.

• I've been slipping them into crumble toppings as a matter of course for years, and it's amazing how appreciative the most sceptical of palates don't seem to complain. They usually ask what the nutty taste is. Adding a few flaked almonds for disguise is a further ruse I've been known to use.

• You can replace up to one third of the flour in most recipes with oats or oat flour. Oats help retain moisture.

• Replace breadcrumbs with oats when making meatballs or meatloaf.

• Use ground oats instead of breadcrumbs, or as a mix, for fish or poultry.

• Use oats in stuffing.

• Add a handful to soup and stew recipes.

DID YOU KNOW?

Oats have a slightly higher fat content than other grains and so it's best not to purchase huge quantities, as they go rancid quicker. They are cheap enough to buy regularly and in addition you can freeze oats or store them in an airtight container. It's best to store them in a cool, dry, dark place. Properly stored oats will last for several months.

Oats are also used in salad dressings, sauce thickeners, ice-cream coatings and stabilizers, baby foods, beverages, baked goods and snack foods.
Oat starch is slow to crystallize, so it is stable from freezing to thawing and holds up well under high temperatures.

PORRIDGE RECIPES

There seem to be as many ways to make your bowl of porridge as there are days in the year. I don't propose to bore you with them all, but my own research into making the best of it, with the least fuss has come up with some useful points. I'm somewhat limited by the requirements of a low fat, no/low sugar regime, but that doesn't stop me drooling on occasions. The interesting thing is that after a while you don't really notice the lack of honey/syrup/brown sugar if there are other good things to flavour the oats, which I know are doing me good all day long.

Some of the following recipes are historical and some hysterical; you can choose which is which.

The origins of Porridge go far back into Scottish history. It used to be either cooked overnight or very early in the morning. Eaten for breakfast, the remainder was left to set in slabs to be eaten later. It is usually made, as below, with milk or water.

A non-stick pan would seem the best vessel to use, unless you have a double saucepan, like the one my grandmother had when I was little. Whatever you use, soak immediately you have finished serving, unless you want to be scouring out the 'hithery dithery', as the poem puts it.

Bear in mind that porridge oats weigh a lot less than medium oatmeal, so that's why the recipes vary somewhat in quantities. Don't use the equivalent amount of medium oatmeal to porridge oats, or you might just have trouble getting up!

Some recipes use cooked oats, so the weight includes water or milk. Just read carefully and substitute quantities for different types of oats. I've based most recipes on one or two servings for convenience.

TRADITIONAL PORRIDGE FOR TWO

You will need:
> 80 g (4 tablespoons) medium oatmeal.
> 450 ml ($^3/_4$ pint) water
> 150 ml ($^1/_4$ pint) milk
> $^1/_2$ teaspoon salt
> 1 tablespoon cream (optional)

Method:
1. Place the salt, water and milk in a medium saucepan. Sprinkle in the oatmeal, stirring all the time and bring to the boil.
2. Turn it down to simmer and stir continuously for 10—15 minutes. The mixture will bubble and thicken, so keep stirring to make sure no lumps form.
3. Remove from the heat and stir in the tablespoon of cream if you are indulging yourself.
4. Serve with brown sugar, honey or treacle, or sweet fruits.

BASIC PORRIDGE
FOR LOW FAT, LOW SUGAR DIETS

After a great deal of trial and error and a lot of reading instructions on the backs of packets, (which seem to split as soon as you try to open them) I've settled for porridge oats like those sold in 500g bags in most high street supermarkets. These are whole grain, offering maximum benefit from a low GI and can be microwaved quickly and without fuss. I've compromised the water/milk argument by using skimmed milk, which, you might be interested to note, has more calcium than semi-skimmed milk, and I need the calcium. Measurements in cups of oats seems more realistic than getting scales out every day, so I hope you follow my logic. Basically the proportions of oats to water or milk is one to three, although I notice that most of the Scottish recipes have a proportion of one to four and American recipes use less liquid. It is a lot easier to add more liquid, however, than to have very runny porridge, as I've found out to my cost.

Using a microwave means less standing and stirring but also less washing up! I'm certain that the purists won't agree. Microwaves vary, and I know mine is more powerful than the average, so be prepared to use the times as a guide only.

Per serving you need:
> $^1/_2$ cup porridge oats
> $1^1/_2$ cups skimmed milk

Method:
1. Mix together the oats and skimmed milk in a fairly large bowl. This will prevent the need for removing concrete from the microwave if it boils over.
2. Microwave on full power for $1^1/_2$ to 2 minutes, depending on the power of your microwave.
3. Stir and allow the porridge to stand. (If you try to eat it now, you'll burn your mouth anyway).
4. If the porridge hasn't thickened sufficiently give it another 20 seconds.
Now comes the best bit; what to add.

• Once you are weaned off sugar even a small drizzle of honey adds to the taste and texture. It's much better than adding artificial sweeteners which may contain aspartame and won't do you any good in the long term.

• Try a sprinkling of raisins and almonds as a sort of hot muesli. Nuts are good for you, one of the superfoods.

• A dozen blueberries, added after the porridge is cooked adds a great, sweet feeling. Blueberries are another of the superfoods, so easily justified. You only need a few for a bowl of porridge, so a punnet will last a few days. I'm sure bananas or most other fruits would do nicely too, but fruit plays a big part of my lunch regime, so I don't want to overdo it for breakfast.

• I go through phases of what to add, but basically the options are fruit, nuts and (I'll say this quietly because I'm not sure it's on the approved list) a square of 85% cocoa solid plain chocolate, which gives a very rich chocolaty colour and pleasant hint of sweetness and naughtiness at breakfast time.

TRADITIONAL SCOTTISH PORRIDGE RECIPE I

You will need:
 1 cup oatmeal
 3 cups of water
 $1^1/_2$ cups milk
 knob of butter
 $^1/_2$ teaspoon of salt

Method:
1. Put oatmeal, water and milk in a pan, stirring all the time.
2. Bring to the boil, add butter and salt.
3. Keep stirring until it thickens.

TRADITIONAL SCOTTISH PORRIDGE RECIPE II

You will need:
110 g (4 oz) oatmeal
150 ml ($^1/_4$ pint) milk
575 ml (1 pint) boiling water
teaspoon salt

Method:
1. Mix the oatmeal and milk together to form a paste, then add the boiling water.
2. Heat and simmer for 15 minutes, stirring occasionally.
3. Stir in the salt and serve.

OLD FASHIONED BAKED PORRIDGE

You could serve this as a dessert, topped with ice cream. This amount serves two. Although the sweet ingredients have been cut by half, they still look a bit much to me!

You will need:
575 ml (1 pint) water
$^1/_4$ teaspoon salt
80 g (3 oz) medium oatmeal
25 g (1 oz) raisins
15 g (1 tablespoon) maple syrup
15 g (1 tablespoon) black treacle
15 g (1 tablespoon) dark brown sugar
15 g (1 tablespoon) walnuts, chopped
1 egg, beaten
$^1/_4$ teaspoon cinnamon
$^1/_4$ teaspoon ground ginger
A pinch of nutmeg
chilled milk or cream

Method:
1. Heat the oven to 180°C.
2. Bring the water to the boil, add salt, reduce heat and sprinkle in the oats.
3. Cook for 5 minutes, stirring frequently.

4. Transfer the oatmeal to an ovenproof dish. Add all the remaining ingredients, (except the milk or cream). Stir well.

5. Bake until set (approximately 40—45 minutes).

6. Spoon into bowls and serve with milk or cream.

THREE GRAIN PORRIDGE

A hot cereal, perfect for cold mornings. It serves two, but may need planning ahead because of the cooking time. Serve with milk and honey and add sliced bananas for extra luxury. It certainly needs something to mop up all that goodness! Served with soya milk it would be suitable for vegans.

You will need:
- 700 ml (1^1/$_4$ pints) water
- 80 g (3 oz) rolled oats
- 80 g (3 oz) rice
- 80 g (3 oz) barley

Method:

1. Bring the water to the boil.

2. Add the grains, lower the heat and simmer for about 45 minutes, stirring occasionally.

ORANGE AND GINGER PORRIDGE

The only difference to this recipe might be to leave out
the caraway seeds, which are a bit of an acquired taste,
especially first thing in the morning.

You will need for two servings:
120 g (8 tablespoons) porridge oats
$^2/_3$ teaspoon ground ginger
$^1/_2$ teaspoon caraway seeds (optional)
4 teaspoons sugar or artificial sweetener
3 teaspoons low-fat yoghurt, crème fraiche or single cream
700 ml (1$^1/_4$ pints) water
2 teaspoons chunky marmalade mixed with 2 teaspoons
   boiling water for a topping

Method:
1. Mix the porridge oats, water, ground ginger and
caraway seeds in a saucepan and bring to the boil.
2. Simmer and stir until thickened.
3. Add sugar or sweetener.
4. Pour into bowls and top with yoghurt or crème fraiche
and the marmalade mixture.

GOLDEN PORRIDGE WITH FRUIT CRUST

The topping is adaptable to whatever fruits and nuts you
want. I think it sounds good as an alternative topping for
a fruit crumble as well, avoiding the use of fats.

You will need for the Porridge:
$^1/_2$ teaspoon salt
80 g (3 oz) medium oatmeal
575 ml (1 pint) water
1 tablespoon treacle
1 tablespoon honey
$^1/_2$ teaspoon cinnamon

You will need for the Crunch Topping:
    1 tablespoon dried currants
    1 tablespoon dried cranberries
    1 tablespoon flaked almonds
    1^1/$_2$ tablespoons sugar
    2 tablespoons oatmeal

Method:
1. Prepare the topping first, by roasting the oatmeal in a dry frying pan, stirring all the time until it goes brown. Add the other topping ingredients and continue to stir.
2. Put water, salt and oats in a pan and bring to the boil. Simmer and stir for about three minutes.
3. Add the milk, treacle, honey and cinnamon and continue to cook, stirring constantly for another three minutes, or until thickened.
4. Serve hot, sprinkled with crunch topping.

You could prepare the crunch topping in advance, especially if you are using the oven. In this case, spread the ingredients out on baking paper and roast for about ten minutes until golden. This can be stored in an airtight container until needed.

STEEL-CUT OAT PORRIDGE WITH PINEAPPLE

Steel cut oats are much grittier than porridge oats, so give a firmer texture. You could substitute the pineapple for raisins or mixed dried fruit.

You will need:
    150 g (5.5 oz) steel cut oats
    320 ml (just over ^{1}/$_2$ pint) water
    1 dessertspoon black treacle
    1 teaspoon brown sugar
    40 g (1^1/$_2$ oz) crushed pineapple with juice
    ^{1}/$_2$ teaspoon cinnamon

Method:
1. Boil the water and sprinkle in the oats and brown sugar.
2. Reduce heat and simmer.

3. Stir in pineapple, juice, treacle and cinnamon.
4. Simmer for 20 minutes, stirring occasionally and adding additional water if necessary to prevent sticking. Cook until the oats are soft.

BABY BEAR'S PORRIDGE THAT WAS JUST RIGHT

You will need:
> 80 g (3 oz) porridge oats, or quick cook oats
> pinch salt
> 575 ml (1 pint) milk
> $^1/_2$ banana
> 40 g (1$^1/_2$ oz) chopped walnuts or raisins
> 2 tablespoons flaked coconut or 2 tablespoons brown sugar

Method:
1. Cook the oats in the milk with salt or according to package directions.
2. Place in serving dishes.
3. Peel the banana and cut into thin slices. Arrange these on top of the porridge. Add the walnuts or raisins.
4. Sprinkle coconut or brown sugar on top of porridge.
5. Serve with extra milk, if necessary.

SPOTTED DICK PORRIDGE

You will need for two servings:
> 75 g (3 oz) medium oatmeal
> 575 ml (1 pint) water
> 5 g (1 tablespoon) wheat bran
> 1 tablespoon sultanas
> 2 large egg whites
> 1 dash vanilla essence
> 1 pinch ground ginger
> 3 medium dried prunes
> 55 g (2 oz) low-fat yoghurt
> sugar or artificial sweetener, to taste
> honey for drizzling

Method:

1. Separate the egg whites into a small bowl and set aside the yolks.
2. Chop the prunes into medium chunks.
3. Put the oats and wheat bran in a saucepan with the ginger and vanilla with the water and bring to the boil.
4. Add the sultanas and simmer, then the prunes.
5. Pour the egg whites into the middle of the porridge and turn up the heat. Don't stir.
6. Using a wooden spoon ease the sides of the porridge to the middle. You want to leave pieces of egg white visible but fully cooked.
7. Spoon into bowls and sprinkle sugar or sweetener over the top.
8. Add a dollop of yoghurt and gently stir in. Add more sugar or sweetener if necessary. Drizzle honey over the top of the porridge before eating.

BLUEBERRIES & CREAM PORRIDGE

You will need:

    80 g (3 oz) oatmeal
    575 ml (1 pint) water
    150 g (5–6 oz) blueberries
    Pinch of cinnamon
    40 ml evaporated milk (optional)

Method:

1. Bring the water to the boil in a small saucepan. Add the oatmeal and cook, stirring until thickened.
2. Add the blueberries and cinnamon. Just before serving, add the evaporated milk.

CHRISTMAS PORRIDGE I

You will need for 2 servings:
    250 g (1 cup) porridge, cooked
    60 ml ('/₄ cup) eggnog
    15 g (1 tablespoon) dried cranberries or raisins
    1 gingersnap biscuit, crumbled (optional)

Method:
After making your porridge in the usual way, add the
other ingredients and serve.

CHRISTMAS PORRIDGE II

This seems too good to only use at Christmas.

You will need (per person):
    110 g (4 oz) porridge oats
    275 ml ('/₂ pint) milk
    knob of butter
    140 g (5 oz) mixed dried fruit selection
    '/₂ miniature bottle of rum
    1 orange, zest only
    double cream

Method:
1. Cook the porridge in the milk over a gentle heat,
stirring all the time.
2. Melt the butter in a pan and sauté the fruit for two or
three minutes. Add the rum and flambé it if you want.
Stir in the orange zest.
3. Pour the porridge into a serving dish and spoon the
flambéed fruit on top.
4. Drizzle with cream to serve.

DANISH CHRISTMAS RICE PORRIDGE

This is a real Danish tradition for Christmas Eve. When the porridge is almost cooked one blanched almond is dropped into the pot. Whoever finds the almond in their bowl wins a small present.

You will need for 2 servings:
425 ml (³/₄ pint) milk
60g (2 oz) short-grain rice
¹/₄ teaspoon salt
sugar
cinnamon

Method:
1. Boil the milk in a heavy saucepan.
2. Add rice to the boiling milk, stirring.
3. Lower the heat, add salt and cover with a lid and gently cook the rice until soft and thickened.
4. Serve with a pat of butter and sprinkle with cinnamon and sugar.

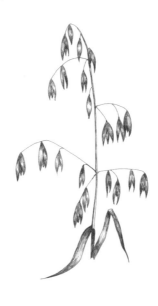

QUICK ORANGE PORRIDGE FOR TWO

This recipe avoids milk altogether, so would suit dairy free diets.

You will need:
80 g (3 oz) porridge oats
300 ml ($^1/_2$ pint) cold unsweetened orange juice

Method:
1. Mix the porridge oats and orange juice in a medium sized microwave-safe bowl.
2. Microwave for 2 minutes, stirring occasionally, until the orange is absorbed. Add more orange juice if necessary.
3. Stir and top with fresh orange slices.

LUXURY CARAMEL PORRIDGE

This recipe suggests the old method of soaking oats overnight. Most other aspects are more modern in approach. The original recipe required making caramelised milk, as for banoffee pie, but a much simpler solution is to buy caramel cream from the supermarket.

You will need:
$1^1/_2$ cups porridge oats
$1^1/_2$ cups water
1 vanilla pod (opened)
2 extra cups water
pinch of salt
30 ml (2 tablespoons) caramel cream
1 tot butterscotch liqueur (or other, to taste)

Method:
1. Soak the porridge oats overnight in the water and vanilla.
2. Next day cook the porridge with the extra water and salt.
3. Stir in the caramel cream and tot of liqueur.
4. Serve with mini marshmallows and double cream.

SWEDISH FIG AND GOATS' BUTTER PORRIDGE

You will need:
    80 g (3 oz) oatmeal
    300 ml ($^1/_2$ pint) water
    2 fresh figs
    3 tablespoons goats' butter, or ordinary butter
    Pinch of salt
    Jam to serve

Method:
1. Bring oatmeal, water and the figs to the boil.
2. Reduce the heat and simmer, adding salt at the end of the cooking.
3. When cooked add the goats' butter and stir for a minute.
4. Put in bowls with jam on the top.

OTHER BREAKFAST RECIPES

HOME MADE GRANOLA

For the uninitiated, granola is the US equivalent of muesli. The basic ingredients are oats, nuts and honey, baked until crispy and then mixed with raisins or dates. The idea is that you prepare a batch of granola and use it as a breakfast food or snack to eat when doing something active and healthy, like hiking or camping. You can eat it with milk as a cereal or poured over yoghurt to give texture and flavour. It is lightweight, high in energy and easy to carry. Over the years the added ingredients have made it into something closer to junk food, with marshmallow, chocolate, peanut butter, and hydrogenated fats. Because there is no flour, however or oil, granolas are high in fibre, if high in sugar as well.

You will need for home made granola:
225 g (8oz) porridge oats
80 g (3 oz) flaked almonds
80 g (3 oz) raisins
80 g (3 oz) cashew nuts
60 g (2 oz) desiccated coconut
2 tablespoons brown sugar
2 tablespoons maple syrup or honey
2 dessertspoons vegetable oil

Method:
1. Mix the oats, nuts, coconut and brown sugar in a large bowl
2. Combine the maple syrup and oil and add to the dry mix.
3. Mix well and pour onto 2 baking sheets
4. Cook for 75 minutes in a very cool oven (130°C, 250°F gas mark just 1). Stir every 15 minutes or so to make the mix brown evenly.
5. Remove from the tins to a large bowl and mix in the raisins. When cool the mix can be stored in a biscuit tin, plastic bag or screw top jar.

BANANA MILKSHAKE

You will need for 2 milkshakes:
225 g (8 oz) instant oats
1 ripe banana
450 ml ($^3/_4$ pint) semi-skimmed or skimmed milk
1 dessertspoon honey

Method:
1. Put all the ingredients in a blender and mix until smooth.
2. Add more skimmed milk to adjust the consistency. Serve chilled.

OATS AND FRUIT BREAKFAST MIX

You may find it convenient to prepare your oatmeal up to a month ahead. In this recipe, you mix together the dry ingredients and just microwave a cupful at a time. I don't know if it will save time in the mornings. I like to choose what to mix into my porridge on a daily basis.

You will need:
400 g (14 oz) porridge oats
30 g (1 oz) raisins
30 g (1 oz) dried fruit
1 tablespoon brown sugar
1 teaspoon cinnamon
pinch of salt

Method:
Combine the first seven ingredients and store in an airtight container.

1. In a deep microwave-proof bowl, put $^1/_2$ cup of porridge mix and $1^1/_2$ cups of water.
2. Microwave on high for one minute and stir.
3. Cook for a further 30—60 seconds or until thickened.
4. Let it stand for one to two minutes before eating.

LUXURY MUESLI

You will need for 2 servings:
150 g (5.5 oz) porridge oats or jumbo oats
1 tablespoon demerara sugar
1 tablespoon chopped, roasted nuts
1 medium apple, cored and chopped
1 banana sliced
150 ml ($^1/_4$ pint) milk
lemon juice (optional)

Method:
1. Mix the dry ingredients.
2. Dip the fruit into lemon juice if you want to prevent browning.
3. Pour the milk over and allow to stand for 10 minutes. to soften the oats slightly before eating.

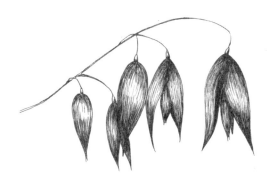

CHAI OATMEAL

Anyone who likes Indian food will probably enjoy this for a change.

You will need for 2 servings:
  150 g (5.5 oz) porridge oats
  pinch of turmeric (up to $^1/_4$ teaspoon ... you decide)
  pinch of salt
  pinch ground coriander
  pinch ground cardamom
  pinch ground cinnamon
  pinch ground allspice
  2 cloves
  pinch nutmeg
  1 teaspoon honey
  350 ml (10 fl oz) milk
  1 tablespoon plain yoghurt

Optional extras:
Finely diced dried fruit, like apricots, cranberries or raisins chopped walnuts or toasted almonds.

Method:
1. Put the oats and spices in a deep, microwave-proof bowl.
2. Add the milk and stir.
3. Cook on high power for 2 minutes, then stir.
4. Continue cooking and stirring at 30 second intervals until the oatmeal is thick.
5. Serve with plain yoghurt (optional).

MAIN COURSE RECIPES

HERRINGS IN OATMEAL

This is a classic way to cook fresh herrings, and it's also doubly healthy, because of the fish oils. When mackerel are plentiful and cheap you could use them instead.

You will need:
   4 herrings, cleaned and gutted
   60—80 g (2—3 oz) fine oatmeal
   50 g (2 oz) butter or margarine
   lemon wedges for serving
   salt and freshly ground white pepper

Method:
1. Season the herrings and press them into the oatmeal on the skin and flesh side, brushing off any excess oats.
2. Heat the butter in a heavy frying pan and cook the herrings for 4—5 minutes on each side until golden.
3. Serve with lemon wedges and preferably with boiled, new potatoes.

ROAST GUINEA FOWL (OR CHICKEN) WITH HAGGIS AND OAT STUFFING

Haggis, mixed with extra oats makes a good stuffing for game and poultry. You don't often see guinea fowl on special offer in the supermarket, but this works equally well for chicken; either one larger bird or two small ones.

You will need for 2—4 servings:
   2 guinea fowl, each weighing about a kilo
   500 g (1 lb) haggis
   1 tablespoon oats
   2 tablespoons chopped parsley
   Knob of butter
   Salt and freshly ground black pepper
   1 onion, quartered
   2 carrots, cut into chunks
   $^1/_2$ tablespoon flour
   500 ml (1 pint) chicken stock
   1 tablespoon whisky (optional)

Method:
1. Pre-heat the oven to 230°C (450°F, gas mark 8).
2. Mix the haggis, oats and parsley together and push the stuffing into the cavities of the guinea fowl or the chicken.
3. Put the vegetables into a roasting tray, rub the fowl with butter and season well. Place the fowl on the vegetables, breasts facing up and cook for 15 minutes.
4. Turn the oven down to 200°C (400°F, gas mark 6) and continue cooking for 40 minutes, basting occasionally. If you have one larger bird you will need to adjust the cooking time accordingly, to ensure the stuffing is cooked properly.
5. Transfer the fowl onto a heated plate and surround it with the vegetables.
6. Put the roasting tray on a low heat on the stove top. Stir the flour into the juices and gradually add the whisky and stock, stirring well. Simmer for about 5 minutes, until the sauce has thickened.

GOLDEN OATS PORK CHOP CASSEROLE

Tasty pork chops on a bed of oats, onions, apple, orange and herbs

You will need:
4 pork chops
1 tablespoon cooking oil
2 onions
2 eating apples, diced
1 orange, peeled and sliced
pinch of thyme
salt and pepper
25 g (1 oz) butter or margarine
175 g (6 oz) porridge oats, uncooked
1 egg
100 ml (4 fl oz) water or broth

Method:
1. Combine the oats and egg in a bowl and mix until the oats are thoroughly coated.

2. Trim any excess fat from the chops and sprinkle with pepper. Brown on both sides in oil.

3. Remove chops from the pan and cook the onion in the same pan with the butter or margarine.

4. Add the oats mixture to the onions, stirring constantly until lightly browned.

5. Add the water, salt, diced apple, orange, thyme and continue cooking, stirring occasionally until the liquid evaporates.

6. Transfer to a casserole dish and arrange the chops on top. Cover and bake at 180°C (350°F, gas mark 4) for about 45 minutes.

CRUNCHY OATMEAL CHICKEN

You will need:
> 2 boneless chicken breasts, halved
> 2 dessertspoons lemon juice
> salt and freshly ground pepper
> 60 g (3 oz) medium oatmeal
> pinch of red chilli powder
> 1 dessertspoon water
> 1 egg white

Method:
1. Marinate the chicken pieces in lemon juice for an hour.

2. Pre-heat oven to 200°C, (400°F, gas mark 6).

3. Mix together the oatmeal, chilli powder, black pepper and salt.

4. In another bowl, lightly whip an egg white with the spoon of water.

5. Drain the chicken pieces well, dip into egg white and then into the oatmeal mixture to coat each piece evenly.

6. Place on a well-greased tray and bake for 20 minutes on each side until the chicken is well browned.

7. Serve hot with tomato or chilli sauce.

MEATLOAF WITH OATS

Oats make a perfect substitute for breadcrumbs. Using minced chicken or turkey makes an excellent substitute for beef, and for the last year I've only used turkey mince for meat loaf, lasagna or pasta sauces. Most people don't notice the difference. Turkey mince is virtually fat free, very cheap to buy and it means the whole family can eat the same thing. I often line the tin with a couple of strips of bacon, making it a lot more salty, but very popular with everyone else.

You will need:
    500 g (1 lb) beef or turkey mince
    3 tablespoons ketchup, or
    2 tablespoons tomato puree
    150 g (5 oz) oats
    1 onion, finely chopped
    1 tablespoon parsley
    $1/2$ teaspoon paprika
    2 sliced back bacon (optional)

Method:
1. Mix all ingredients together in a large bowl.
2. Line a loaf tin with bacon, or grease the tin.
3. Pack in the meat mix and bake at 180°C (350°F, gas mark 4) for 45 minutes—1 hour.
4. Turn out onto a plate to serve, with seasonal vegetables.

SPICY PRAWNS WITH OATMEAL BUTTER

I can feel my cholesterol rising at the thought of this recipe, and even the oats won't do too much good, being of the quick cook variety. However, it sounds interesting, if you can eat what you like.

You will need for 2 servings:
300 g (10.5 oz) cooked prawns
45 g (1^1/$_2$ oz) butter or margarine
3 egg yolks, beaten lightly
1 tablespoon chopped garlic
1 tablespoon shallots
1 teaspoon instant chicken bouillon granules
^{1}/$_2$ teaspoon sugar
pinch of curry
2 hot chilli peppers (or to taste)
salt and pepper, to taste
75 g (3 oz) quick cook oatmeal

Method:
1. Sauté egg yolks in the butter or margarine and add garlic, chicken stock granules, sugar, curry leaves, chillies, salt and pepper.
2. Continue to fry till fragrant. Add the prawns and stir.
3. Lastly, add the oatmeal and fry until dry. Serve hot.

TURKEY STUFFING

This Scottish stuffing works well in turkey or chicken. The quantities obviously depend on the size of the bird, so adjust accordingly.

You will need:
225 g (8 oz) oatmeal
1 small onion
60 g (2 oz) margarine or butter, melted
pinch of sage
1 garlic clove
salt
pepper

Method:
1. Dice the onion and crush the garlic.
2. Mix oatmeal, salt, pepper, sage, onion, and garlic.
3. Mix in the butter or margarine then stuff the bird with the mixture.

OATMEAL TURKEY STUFFING OR SKIRLIE

You will need:
  1 onion
  3 stalks celery
  80 g (3 oz) butter
  500 g (1 lb) oatmeal
  sage
  thyme
  garlic powder
  salt
  pepper
  pinch of nutmeg
  water, to moisten

Method:
1. Dice the onion and celery. Melt the butter in a frying pan and sauté onions and celery until soft.
2. Add the oatmeal and seasonings and stir until well mixed.
3. Mix with water until clumps are formed. Gently pack into the turkey cavity.

You can also make this as a side dish if you steam it in the pan. Made like that, it's called skirlie.

ROOT VEGETABLE CRUMBLE

For this recipe you can use any seasonal root vegetables, or add a slightly more exotic feel by using sweet potatoes, plantain and even more spices. Don't worry if you haven't got all of the root vegetables: this is just a guide.

You will need for 6 servings:
   2 onions, peeled and roughly chopped
   2 cloves of garlic, peeled and crushed
   1 teaspoon thyme
   1 teaspoon cumin seeds
   50 g (2 oz) butter or margarine
   1 tablespoon flour
   1 litre (2 pints) vegetable stock
   1 parsnip, peeled and cut into 2 cm (1 in) chunks
   1 small swede, diced
   2 carrots, diced
   2 turnips, diced
   salt and freshly ground black pepper
   $^1/_2$ celeriac root, diced

For the crust:
   60 g (2 oz) butter or margarine
   60 g (2 oz) breadcrumbs
   2 tablespoons grated, mature cheese
   60 g (2 oz) porridge oats
   2 tablespoons chopped parsley

Method:
1. Pre-heat the oven to 200°C (400°F, gas mark 6).
2. On the hob gently cook the onion, garlic, thyme and cumin in the butter or margarine until soft.
3. Add the flour and stir well, gradually pouring in the vegetable stock a little at a time to prevent lumps forming. Add the vegetables, season and simmer for 20—25 minutes, until the vegetables are tender. There should be just enough sauce left to bind the vegetables, if not turn the heat up to reduce it a little.
4. Meanwhile make the crust. Mix the breadcrumbs, oatmeal and parsley with melted butter or margarine. Pre-heat the oven to 200°C (400°F, gas mark 6).
5. Transfer the vegetables to an oven-proof dish and spoon on the topping to cover the vegetables. Top with grated cheese and bake for 30—40 minutes, until golden.

ROASTED VEGETABLE FETA FLAN

This flan is much lower in fat than a traditional quiche and can be served with new potatoes or bread.

You will need:
   120 g (4 oz) self-raising flour
   50 g (2 oz) oatmeal
   75 g (3 oz) margarine
   2 peppers (1 red and 1 yellow)
   1 courgette
   1 aubergine
   1 red onion
   1 tablespoon olive oil
   1 clove garlic, crushed
   2 tablespoons fresh oregano
   75 g (3 oz) feta cheese, crumbled
   25 g (1 oz) pine nuts
   salt and freshly ground black pepper

Method:
1. Preheat the oven to 200°C (400°F, gas mark 6).
2. Chop the peppers, courgette, aubergine and onion into large chunks.

3. Sift the flour into a large bowl. Stir in the oatmeal, then rub in the margarine until the mixture resembles fine breadcrumbs. Stir in enough water to mix to a dough.
4. Roll out on a lightly floured surface to make a 20 cm round and line a flan dish. Chill for 15 minutes, then bake blind for 15 minutes, until golden.
5. Place all the prepared vegetables into a roasting tin, drizzle over the oil and add the garlic. Put in the oven and roast for 25—30 minutes until tender and slightly charred on the edges.
6. Spoon the roasted vegetables over the pastry base. Sprinkle over the feta, herbs, seasoning and pine nuts and return to the oven for 10 minutes until the cheese is melted. Serve warm or cold

SPEEDY OATMEAL BURGERS

These meatless burgers are quick and easy.

You will need for 4 burgers:
225 g (8 oz) oatmeal
$^1/_2$ teaspoon salt
1 teaspoon sage
1 medium onion, chopped
3 eggs
1 can reduced fat cream soup, eg tomato or asparagus
300 ml (10 fl oz) water

Method:
1. Mix the oatmeal salt, and sage and then add the chopped onion and eggs.
2. Drop large spoonfuls onto a hot non-stick frying pan. Brown on both sides.
3. Mix soup and water, pour over burgers. Cover and simmer on low heat for 20 minutes.

CHEESE AND ONION OAT FLAN

I love this combination of cheese and onion, although there's a lot of fat, what with the cheese, milk and margarine. Using skimmed milk will keep down the fat, and you could use a low fat cheese, as long as it doesn't taste like soap. Still, the oats will do you good!

You will need:
> 120 g (4 oz) wholemeal flour
> 120 g (4 oz) oatmeal
> 120 g (4 oz) margarine
> water for mixing
> pinch of salt
> 2 eggs
> 3 chopped onions
> 150 ml ($^{1}/_{4}$ pint) skimmed milk
> 225 g (8 oz) grated cheese of your choice
> pepper

Method:
1. Put the flour, salt and oatmeal into a large bowl and rub in the margarine.
2. Add enough water to mix to a firm dough.
3. Turn onto a floured surface, knead and roll out to line a flan dish.
4. Put in the fridge while you make the filling.
5. Heat some oil in a pan to fry the chopped onions. Fry until they start to turn brown.
6. Beat the eggs and add the milk, then the onions and most of the cheese.
7. Put into the pastry crust, add the rest of the cheese and a good pinch or grinding of pepper.
8. Bake at 190°C (375°F, gas mark 5) for 35–40 minutes.

SPANISH OATS

An alternative to rice

You will need for 3—4 servings:
    1 teaspoon extra virgin olive oil
    1 tin tomatoes
    1 teaspoon chilli powder
    2 cloves garlic, finely chopped
    1 medium onion, chopped
    120 g (4 oz) porridge oats
    450 ml (15 fl oz) water

Method:
1. Heat the olive oil in a medium saucepan. Add the garlic and onion and cook until soft.
2. Add the remaining ingredients. Bring to a boil over medium heat.
3. Cover, reduce heat and simmer until the oats are tender and the liquid is absorbed, stirring occasionally.
4. Remove from heat and let stand, covered, for 5 minutes before serving.

POTATO RISSOLES

You will need:
    500 g (1 lb) potatoes, peeled
    1 onion, chopped
    1 egg
    75 g (3 oz) grated Cheddar cheese
    100 g (4 oz) Scottish oatmeal
    salt
    pepper

Method:
1. Boil and mash the potatoes and mix with the onion, cheese, seasoning and half of a beaten egg. Allow to cool.
2. When cool, shape into patties, dip in the remaining egg, then in oatmeal to coat.
3. Cook the patties in vegetable or olive oil for 2—3 minutes on each side, until brown.

CAKES, SCONES, BREADS & BISCUITS

As with all recipes, the quantities for ingredients are given in metric and equivalent imperial measures. There will be small discrepancies between equivalent quantities, so choose either the metric or imperial and don't switch within a recipe.

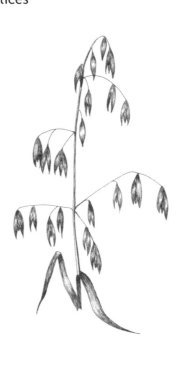

FLAPJACKS

These are most delicious and a great way of getting children to eat oats. You can add chocolate chips instead of walnuts. The possibilities are endless, if you can eat lots of sweet goodies, that is.

You will need:

125 g (4 oz) soft margarine
75 g (3 oz) dark brown sugar
45 ml (3 tablespoons) golden syrup
250 g (8 oz) porridge oats
50 g (2 oz) walnut pieces (optional)

Method:
1. Preheat the oven to 180°C (350°F, gas mark 4).
2. Lightly grease a shallow tin.
3. Melt the margarine, syrup and sugar together in a saucepan.
4. Stir in the oats and walnuts.
5. Place the mixture into the prepared tin and smooth the top with the wooden spoon.
6. Bake in the oven for 25–30 minutes.
7. Cool in the tin for a few minutes and then cut into bars or squares. Cool completely before removing from the tin.

HONEY FLAPJACKS

You will need:

200 g (7 oz) butter
200 g (7 oz) demerara sugar
200 g (7 oz) honey
400 g (14 oz) porridge oats
50 g (1$^3/_4$ oz) nuts, dried fruits, glacé cherries, chopped or desiccated coconut (optional)

Method:
1. Heat the butter, sugar and honey until the sugar has dissolved.
2. Add the oats and nuts, fruit, or coconut and mix well.

3. Place in a greased swiss roll tin or cake tin and spread to about 2 cm (³/₄ in) thick.

4. Bake in a preheated oven at 180°C (350°F, gas mark 4) for 15—20 minutes, until golden around the edges, but soft in the middle. Let it cool in the tin, then turn out and cut into squares.

OATCAKES

These simple oatcakes are easy to make and very good for you. They can be served with butter, low fat cream cheese or hummus. If you prefer, use a cutter to make individual oatcakes.

You will need:

350 g (12 oz) fine oatmeal
1 teaspoon salt
150 ml (¹/₄ pint) boiling water
40 g (1¹/₂ oz) soft margarine
pinch bicarbonate of soda

Method:

1. Put the oats, salt, and bicarbonate of soda into a large bowl.
2. Melt the margarine in water over a low heat.
3. Add to the oats and mix to a dough.
4. Turn out onto sprinkled oatmeal and knead until you have a smooth dough.
5. Dust a rolling pin with oatmeal, halve the dough roll out into two 25 cm (10 in) rounds.
6. Cut each into 8 sections and place onto greased baking sheets.
7. Bake in a cool oven 150°C (300°F, gas mark 2) for 1 hour until crisp. Cool on a wire rack.

SCHOOL DINNER OAT COOKIES

This recipe takes me back to my first teaching job, when the school cook provided freshly baked biscuits to go with jelly or blancmange. This is the recipe, as given to me, over 30 years ago. It was cut down from catering sized portions, hence the unusual amounts. You must try them, they're brilliant! This quantity makes about 20 biscuits.

You will need: **Makes 20 biscuits**

    125 g (4 oz) porridge oats
    125 g (4 oz) butter for margarine
    125 g (4 oz) castor sugar
    125 g (4 oz) plain flour
    pinch bicarbonate of soda
    10 g (^{1}/$_4$oz) baking powder
    35 g (1^1/$_4$ oz) golden syrup

Method:
1. Cream together the margarine and sugar.
2. Add the oats and remaining dry ingredients.
3. Mix with golden syrup.
4. Portion into small balls and place on greased tins allowing room to spread.
5. Bake in a moderate oven 180°C (350°F, gas mark 4) for 15–20 minutes.

OATMEAL COOKIES

You will need: **Makes 30 cookies**

    225 g (8 oz) butter or margarine
    225 g (8 oz) brown sugar, firmly packed
    60 g (2 oz) non fat dry milk powder
    1 large egg
    1 teaspoon vanilla
    1 tablespoon hot water
    ^{1}/$_2$ teaspoon baking soda
    1 pinch salt
    225 g (8 oz) plain flour
    350 g (12 oz) oatmeal

Optional extras:
> 100 g (3^1/$_2$ oz) raisins
> 100 g (3 ^{1}/$_2$ oz) walnut pieces
> 200 g (7 oz) chocolate chips

Method:
1. Preheat the oven to 180°C (350°F, gas mark 4).
2. Cream the butter or margarine with the sugar and milk powder, then add egg and vanilla.
3. Mix the water with baking soda and stir into the mix.
4. Fold in the salt, flour, oatmeal and raisins, walnuts or chocolate chips.
5. Roll dough into small balls and place on a greased baking sheet. Press flat.
6. Bake for 12–15 minutes, until golden brown.

OATMEAL MUFFINS

Surprisingly tasty without any spices or flavourings. The oats need to soak for 1 hour before preparing the recipe.

You will need: **Makes 12 muffins**
> 225 g (8 oz) porridge oats
> 225 ml (8 fl oz) buttermilk or skimmed milk
> 1 egg
> 125 g (4 oz) brown sugar
> 125 g (4 oz) soft margarine, melted
> 225 g (8 oz) plain flour
> ^{1}/$_2$ teaspoon salt
> 1 teaspoon baking powder
> ^{1}/$_2$ teaspoon bicarbonate of soda

Method
1. Soak the oats in the milk for 1 hour.
2. Add beaten egg and mix well.
3. Add sugar and melted margarine, mixing well.
4. Fold in sifted flour, baking powder and bicarbonate of soda.
5. Bake in greased tins or papers at 200°C (400°F, gas mark 6) for 15–20 minutes.

LOW FAT OATMEAL MUFFINS

This variation uses less sugar and has a lower fat content. Healthy stuff!

You will need:
225 g (8 oz) plain flour
60 g (2 oz) sugar
1 egg
1 teaspoon baking powder
$^1/_2$ teaspoon salt
225 g (8 oz) oatmeal
225 ml (8 fl oz) water
45 ml (3 tablespoons) corn oil
pinch of nutmeg or cinnamon

Method:
1. Mix together the beaten egg, oil, sugar and water.
2. Sift the flour, baking powder, spice and salt and add the oats.
3. Combine wet and dry ingredients, stirring just enough to moisten the oats.
4. Put into greased tins or paper liners, up to $^2/_3$ full.
5. Bake at 425°C (220°F, gas mark 7) for about 15 minutes.

OATMEAL BREAD

You will need: **Makes 2 loaves**
225 g (8 oz) porridge oats
45 g (1$^1/_2$ oz) margarine
1 tablespoon salt
45 g (3 tablespoons) treacle
125 g (4 oz) sugar
450 ml ($^3/_4$ pint) boiling water
1 sachet dried yeast
1 tablespoon sugar
125 ml (4 fl oz) water, lukewarm
1.4 kg (3 lb) strong flour

Method:
1. Pour the boiling water over the oats, margarine, salt, treacle and 125 g sugar. Let this stand until lukewarm.
2. Dissolve the yeast and tablespoon of sugar in lukewarm water and add to the oat mixture.
3. Add sifted flour and knead until firm.
4. Leave the dough to rise in a warm place until double the size.
5. Knock out the air, knead and form into 2 loaves. Leave to rise again until it has doubled in volume.
6. Bake at 180°C (350°F, gas mark 4) for 1 hour, or until brown and hollow when knocked.

OATMEAL CARAMELITAS

This sounds a bit complicated, so read through the whole recipe before you start. It involves partially cooking then adding caramel milk topping mixed with flour as a sandwich layer in the middle before completing the process.

You will need: Makes 10—12 bars

300 g (11 oz) plain flour
75 g (2^1/$_2$ oz) plain flour
300 g (11 oz) oatmeal
225 g (8 oz) brown sugar
^{1}/$_2$ teaspoon baking soda
^{1}/$_2$ teaspoon salt
225 g (8 oz) butter or margarine, melted
225 g (8 oz) chocolate chips
150 g (5 oz) chopped walnuts
^{2}/$_3$ jar caramel topping

Method:
1. Preheat oven to 180°C (350°F, gas mark 4). Grease a swiss roll tin or baking dish.
2. Combine the main quantity of flour, oats, brown sugar, baking soda, salt and butter in a large bowl.
3. Press half the mixture into the bottom of the baking dish and bake for 10 minutes.
4. Sprinkle chocolate chips and walnuts over the base.

5. Mix the caramel topping with the rest of the flour and mix well. Pour this over the chocolate chips and nuts.
6. Sprinkle the remaining oat mixture evenly over the base and bake for about 20 minutes.
7. Cool completely before cutting into bars.

PEANUT BUTTER AND OATMEAL NO BAKE COOKIES

These no bake cookies are certainly low in fat, if rather high in sugar. I think reducing the sugar might be a good idea.

You will need:

700 g (24 oz) oatmeal
75 g (2$^1/_2$ oz) low fat peanut butter
10 ml (1 dessertspoon) vanilla essence
450 g (16 oz) brown sugar
120 ml skimmed milk
60 g (2 oz) butter

Method
1. Mix the oats, peanut butter and vanilla.
2. Put the sugar, milk and butter in a saucepan. Heat gently until ingredients are melted, then boil for one minute.
3. Pour over the oatmeal mixture and stir rapidly.
4. Place heaped tablespoons onto plates or trays and leave to cool and set.

HONEY AND OAT BREAD

This is a yeast free recipe, so takes less time to prepare.

You will need:
>   350 g (12 oz) plain flour
>   150 g (6 oz) porridge oats
>   1 dessertspoon baking powder
>   1 teaspoon salt
>   1 egg
>   2 tablespoons honey
>   175 ml (6 fl oz) milk
>   1 teaspoon melted butter

Method:
1. Preheat the oven to 180°C (350°F, gas mark 4) and grease a loaf tin.
2. Put the flour, oats, baking powder and salt in a bowl.
3. Beat together the egg, honey and milk and add to the flour and oats, stirring well.
4. Pour into the loaf tin and bake for about 75 minutes, or until crusty and hollow when knocked.
5. Pour the melted butter over the hot loaf and turn out onto a cooling rack

CHINESE 5-SPICE OATMEAL COOKIES

Chinese 5-spice is a blend of aromatic seasonings and includes the licoricy taste of star anise.

You will need:
>   150 g (5.5 oz) rolled oats
>   120 g (4 oz) plain flour
>   80 g (3 oz) coarsely ground almonds

$^1/_2$ teaspoon Chinese five spice powder

pinch of salt

pinch of baking power

pinch of cinnamon

80 g (3 oz) butter or margarine

80 g (3 oz) granulated sugar

80 g (3 oz) brown sugar

1 egg

1 teaspoon vanilla extract

Method:

1. Preheat oven to 180°C (350°F, gas mark 4).
2. Mix together the oats, flour, almonds, 5-spice powder, cinnamon, baking powder, and salt.
3. Cream the butter or margarine with both sugars until light and smooth. Add the eggs and vanilla and beat well.
4. Fold the flour mixture into the butter mixture.
5. Drop mounded tablespoonfuls onto a lightly greased baking sheet, leaving a gap between each portion for spreading.
6. Bake for 12–15 minutes and cool on wire racks.

SODA BREAD WITH OATS

You will need:

450 g (1 lb) plain flour

1 teaspoon bicarbonate of soda

pinch of salt

1 dessertspoon baking powder

1 teaspoon sugar

150 g (5.5 oz) oat bran

200 g (7 oz) porridge oats

175 ml (6 fl oz) skimmed milk or buttermilk

1 dessertspoon lemon juice

2 tablespoons melted margarine

1 egg, slightly beaten

Method:

1. Preheat the oven to 180°C (350°F, gas mark 4) and grease a baking sheet.

2. Mix the flour, soda, salt, baking powder, sugar and oats in large bowl. Form a well in the middle.

3. In a separate bowl, mix the milk, lemon juice, melted margarine, and egg and gradually add to the dry ingredients.

4. Mix until a dough begins to form. You may need a drop more milk. Knead into a ball on a lightly floured surface.

5. Put the dough onto a baking sheet and make two cuts with a knife to form a cross. Bake for 45–60 minutes. The time depends on the wetness of the dough.

CHEESE SCONES

You will need:

120 g (4 oz) oatmeal

120 g (4 oz) plain flour

60 g (2 oz) grated, mature cheese of choice

1 teaspoon baking powder

pinch of salt

pinch of paprika

40 g (1$^1/_2$ oz) margarine

1 egg

150 ml ($^1/_4$ pint) milk

Method:

1. Preheat the oven to 230°C (450°F, gas mark 8).

2. Sift the flour, salt, pepper and baking powder and mix with the oats.

3. Rub in the margarine, then mix in the grated cheese.

4. Mix the beaten egg with the milk and add to the rest of the ingredients to make a soft dough.

5. Knead lightly, turn onto a floured board and roll out to about 2 cm ($^3/_4$ in) and cut into 5 cm (2 in) rounds with a cutter or small glass. Knead the offcuts of dough gently to finish cutting, but don't handle them too much.

6. Brush with milk and bake for approximately 12 minutes. Serve warm.

CHOCOLATE OAT BARS

This recipe has a slightly unusual method of partially cooking the mix and then adding extra ingredients.

You will need:

225 g (8 oz) plain flour
225 g (8 oz) quick-cooking oats
175 g (6 oz) brown sugar
120g (4 oz) soft margarine
$1/_2$ small can condensed milk
225 g (8 oz) chocolate chips
optional nuts

Method:

1. Preheat oven to 180°C (350°F, gas mark 4).
2. Combine flour, oats, brown sugar and melted margarine. Mix well.
3. Put $2/_3$ of the mixture into a baking tray and bake for 10 minutes.
4. Pour condensed milk evenly over the base and sprinkle with chocolate chips and nuts (optional).Top with remaining oat mixture and press down.
5. Bake for 25—30 minutes or until lightly browned. Cool and slice.

CHOCOLATE OAT BITES

This one is more conventional.

You will need:
>   100 g (4 oz) soft margarine
>   50 g (2 oz) brown sugar
>   3 tablespoons golden syrup
>   175 g (6 oz) porridge oats
>   50 g (2 oz) chocolate drops

Method:
1. Cream the margarine and sugar together.
2. Add the golden syrup, oats and chocolate. Stir thoroughly.
3. Put the mix into a greased cake tin and smooth the top with a spoon.
4. Bake at 200°C (400°F, gas mark 6) for 20 minutes.
5. Leave in the tin to cool and then cut into bars or slices.

OATMEAL PANCAKES

You will need:
>   200 g (7 oz) oatmeal
>   225 ml (8 fl oz) buttermilk
>   1 egg, beaten
>   60 g (2 oz) flour
> $1/2$ teaspoon sugar
> $1/2$ teaspoon baking powder
> $1/2$ teaspoon salt

Method:
1. Mix the oatmeal, sugar, flour, salt and baking powder.
2. Add the beaten egg and half the buttermilk.
3. Beat well and then add the rest of the milk.
4. Spoon small amounts onto a heated, greased griddle, allowing room between pancakes for spreading.
5. Fry until the edges brown. Turn carefully and cook for another minute. Remove to a warm plate while you cook the rest. Serve warm with butter.

GRANOLA BARS

With this recipe you can add or subtract ingredients to suit what you have in the cupboard. You can use dates or mixed dried fruit, or half and half and the nuts can be walnuts, hazelnuts, almonds, or a mix. I don't think the overall effect will be spoiled at all.

You will need:
>   470 g (1 lb) porridge oats
>   60 g (2 oz) desiccated coconut
>   60 g (2 oz) oat bran
>   60 g (2 oz) sunflower seeds
>   60 g (2 oz) chopped dates or dried fruit
>   60 g (2 oz) chopped nuts
>   30 g (1 oz) margarine
>   80 g (3 oz) brown sugar
>   1 tablespoon flour
>   60 g (2 oz) golden or maple syrup
>   2 tablespoons honey
>   pinch of cinnamon

Method:
1. Mix the oats, sunflower seeds coconut, fruit and nuts in a large bowl.
2. Melt the margarine, syrup, sugar, cinnamon and honey together. Let it come to a full boil.
3. Stir into the oats, fruit and nuts. This will be a stiff mixture.
4. Transfer to a greased baking tray or swiss roll tin. Press very firmly and leave it to set.
5. Cut into bars.

FRUITY OAT DROPS

You will need:
>   250 g porridge oats
>   2 tablespoons treacle or honey
>   60 g (2 oz) nuts, chopped
>   60 g (2 oz) raisins
> $^1/_2$ can condensed milk

Method:
1. Mix condensed milk, treacle and oats in a pan until thickened, stirring frequently.
2. Allow to cool, then add nuts and raisins.
3. Drop spoonfuls onto a buttered baking sheet. Allow room for spreading.
4. Bake for 15 minutes at 180°C (350°F, gas mark 4) and remove from the pan immediately. Serve warm.

CRANBERRY OATS BARS

You will need:

225 g (8 oz) old fashioned oats
25 g (1 oz) butter or margarine
120 g (4 oz) light brown sugar
1 egg
1 tablespoon milk
1 teaspoon vanilla essence
120 g (4 oz) flour
pinch of nutmeg
pinch of salt
pinch of baking soda
225 g (8 oz) chopped pecans
150 g dried (6 oz) dried, chopped cranberries

Method:
1. Preheat oven to 180°C (350°F, gas mark 4) and butter a square baking tin.
2. Toast the oatmeal in a dry frying pan, stirring occasionally, until golden.
3. Beat the butter and sugar until fluffy. Beat in the egg, milk and vanilla.
4. Fold in the flour, nutmeg, salt and baking soda.
5. Stir in oatmeal, pecans, and cranberries and put into the baking tin.
6. Bake until golden — about 30—35 minutes. Cool in the pan for 20 minutes, then cut into 12 bars.

FRUITY OAT CAKE

You can use banana, pear, apple, apricot or pineapple in this cake. You need to chop the fruit finely. There's no added sugar, no eggs and very little fat, so that's another bonus.

You will need:

    450 g (1 lb bananas) or
    225 g (8 oz) bananas and 225 g (8 oz) other fruit
    60 g (2 oz) chopped nuts
    120 ml (4 fl oz) cooking oil
    120 g (4 oz) raisins
    80 g (3 oz) porridge oats
    150 g (5 oz) plain flour
    $^1/_2$ teaspoon almond essence
    pinch of salt

Method:
1. Mix all the ingredients together.
2. Spoon into a greased loaf tin.
3. Bake in a pre-heated oven at 190°C (375°F, gas mark 5) for about an hour. Cool before turning out.

ORANGE, OAT AND DATE BARS

You need a blender for this recipe to make the filling nice and smooth.

You will need:

    225 g (8 oz) dried dates
    175 g (6 oz) plain flour
    175 g (6 oz) porridge oats
    175 g (6 oz) margarine
    1 tablespoon honey
    1 orange
    50–70 ml (2–3 fl oz) water

Method:
1. Grate the zest from the orange and peel off the rind.
2. Put the chopped dates, zest and orange segments into

a pan with the water. Cook for 10 minutes, until soft, then cool.

3. Put into a blender and mix to a smooth paste.

4. Mix together the oats and flour, rub in the margarine and add honey to form a dough. Divide into two parts and roll out into rectangles.

5. Spread half of this mixture in the bottom of a greased swiss roll tin. Cover with the date and orange paste and top with the second portion of oats and flour. Press down.

6. Bake at 200°C (400°F, gas mark 6) for about 25 minutes. Cool before cutting into slices.

BROONIE

Fine oatmeal gives this mild gingerbread a texture like wholemeal bread. Try eating it warm.

You will need:

175 g (6 oz) fine oatmeal

175 g (6 oz) plain flour

60 g (2 oz) butter or margarine

1 egg

1 teaspoon ground ginger

2 tablespoons treacle

1 teaspoon baking soda

150 ml (¹/₄ pint) milk

Method:

1. Sift the flour, ginger and baking soda and mix with the oatmeal.

2. Melt the butter or margarine with the treacle and add to the oat mix.

3. Stir well and add the egg, well beaten.

4. Gradually stir in the milk.

5. Pour into a greased loaf tin and bake at 200°C (400°F, gas mark 6) for 60—80 minutes. It should be well risen and firm on top.

PARKIN

This cake hails from the North of England. When we lived in Yorkshire the locals ate it with cheese and apple, as they do fruit cake.

You will need:

   120 g (4 oz) butter or margarine
   120 g (4 oz) medium oatmeal
   225 g (8 oz) porridge oats
   120 g (4 oz) plain flour
   3 teaspoons ground ginger
   ¹/₂ teaspoon bicarbonate of soda
   ¹/₂ teaspoon baking powder
   pinch of salt
   2 eggs
   150 ml (¹/₄ pint) molasses or treacle
   15 ml (1 tablespoon) honey
   75 ml (3 fl oz) milk
   75 ml (3 fl oz) apple juice

Method:
1. Grease and line a square 20 cm (8 in) baking tin. Preheat the oven to 170°C (325°F, gas mark 3).
2. Mix the flour, oats, salt, ginger, baking powder and bicarb together in a large bowl.
3. Put the butter/margarine, molasses/treacle and honey into a saucepan and bring to the boil, stirring to mix.
4. Add to the dry ingredients and mix.
5. Put the milk, eggs and apple juice into the pan and heat gently. It may curdle, but don't worry.
6. Add this mix to the bowl, stir well and pour into the baking tin.
7. Bake for about 30—35 minutes. Cool and cut into squares.

OAT ROLLS

You will need:

25 g (1 oz) fresh yeast or
1 sachet dried yeast and 2 tablespoons warm water
1 tablespoon honey
425 ml ($^3/_4$ pint) skimmed milk
225 g (8 oz) oatmeal
450 g (1 lb) wholemeal or plain flour
1 teaspoon salt

Method:

1. Mix the yeast with the honey. Warm the milk and stir in the oatmeal. Add the yeast to the oats and leave to stand for an hour.
2. Stir in the flour and salt and knead to form a dough. It should be soft but not too dry. Leave to rest for 30 minutes.
3. Knead again for a couple of minutes. Don't be heavy handed.
4. Divide into 12 portions and make into balls. Make a dent in the centre of each one.
5. Leave to rise for another 30 minutes on a greased baking tray and preheat the oven to 220°C (425°F, gas mark 7).
6. Bake for 15–20 minutes until the rolls sound hollow when knocked. Cool on a rack.

PEANUT BUTTER AND OAT BISCUITS

There seem to be plenty of variations on the theme of 'What else that is sweet and fatty can I put in my cookies to make them extra yummy?' baking. This recipe is a compromise, containing fewer oats, but also less sugar and fat. Chocolate optional.

You will need:

120 g (4 oz) soft margarine
120 g (4 oz) brown sugar
120 g (4 oz) low fat peanut butter
120 g (4 oz) medium oatmeal

1 egg
1 teaspoon vanilla essence
225 g (8 oz) plain or wholemeal flour
1 teaspoon bicarbonate of soda
pinch of salt
120 g (4 oz) chocolate chips (optional)

Method:
1. Cream together the margarine and sugar and add peanut butter, vanilla and egg.
2. Mix the dry ingredients together and combine with the cream mix.
3. Roll into small balls and bake for 10–12 minutes at 180°C (350°F, gas mark 4). Cool on the tray.
You could add 120 g (4 oz) of chocolate chips to the dough, if you really must have chocolate with your peanuts.

BLUEBERRY, YOGHURT AND OATMEAL MUFFINS

You will need:
2 eggs, beaten
225 ml (8 oz) plain, low fat yoghurt
60 g (2 oz) margarine
300 g (10^1/$_2$ oz) plain flour
225 g (8 oz) oats
120 g (4 oz) brown sugar
1 dessertspoon baking powder
1 teaspoon cinnamon
^{1}/$_2$ teaspoon bicarbonate of soda
pinch nutmeg
pinch salt
225 g (8 oz) blueberries

Method:
1. Preheat the oven to 200°C (400°F, gas mark 6) and prepare 12 muffin tins or papers.
2. Mix all ingredients together except the blueberries. Don't worry about lumps but make sure all the flour is moistened.
3. Fold in the fruit and divide evenly between muffin cases. Bake for 20–25 minutes, until golden.

OAT AND SESAME BISCUITS

Another healthy, low fat recipe to try.

You will need:

150 g (5^1/$_2$ oz) medium oats
2 tablespoons sesame seeds
75 g (3 oz) brown sugar
125 ml (4 fl oz) cooking oil

Method:
1. Roast the sesame seeds in a dry pan until golden.
2. Put the oats, sesame seeds, sugar and oil in a bowl and leave for 1 hour.
3. Add the beaten egg and stir well.
4. Put small spoonfuls of mixture onto a greased baking tray with plenty of room to spread.
Bake at 170°C (325°F, gas mark 3) for 15–20 minutes.
Leave to cool a little before moving to a cooling rack.

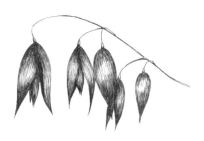

MALTED OAT SLICES

Nutty, healthy and delicious.

You will need:
- 250 g (8 oz) porridge oats
- 125 ml (4 fl oz) vegetable oil
- 45 ml (3 tablespoons) malt extract
- 50 g (2 oz) brown sugar
- 2 tablespoons sesame seeds

Method:
1. Roast the sesame seeds in a dry pan until golden.
2. Put the oil, malt extract and sugar in a pan and heat gently.
3. Add the remaining ingredients and mix.
4. Press into a greased baking tin and smooth down.
5. Bake at 180°C (350°F, gas mark 4) for about 30 minutes.
6. Cool in the tin a little and then cut into slices. Leave in the tin until completely cool.

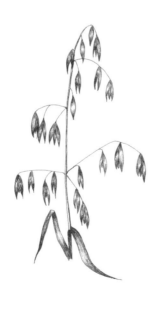

DESSERT RECIPES

IRISH OATMEAL

You will need for 4 servings:

450 ml ($^3/_4$ pint) water
pinch salt
60 g (2 oz) butter
450 g (1 lb) rolled oats
80 g (3 oz) light corn syrup
4 tablespoons brandy
225 g (8 oz) raisins
120 ml cream
60g (2 oz) light brown sugar
225g (8 oz) fresh fruit (blueberries, raspberries, blackberries)

Method:
1. Heat corn syrup and brandy over a medium heat and bring to a simmer.
2. Add the raisins and simmer for 3–5 minutes. Set aside to cool.
3. Boil the water with the salt, then add the butter and oats.
4. Lower the heat and simmer until oats are tender – about 6–10 minutes.
5. Place 2 tablespoons of cream, 1 tablespoon of brown sugar and 1tablespoon of drained raisins in each bowl. Add steaming, cooked oats and top with fresh berries. Each person stirs their bowl to enjoy the hidden surprise waiting underneath.

APRICOT CRUNCH

Juicy apricots with a light crunchy topping, a quick dessert using store cupboard ingredients.
Use fresh apricots, or other fruit when in season.

You will need for 6 servings:

2 x 300 g cans apricots in fruit juice, drained
grated rind and juice of 1 large orange
50 g (2 oz) rolled oats
1 tablespoon demerara sugar
25 g (1 oz) flaked almonds

1 tablespoon melted butter
1 tablespoon sesame seeds
1 tablespoon runny honey

Method:
1. Preheat the oven to 200°C (400°F, gas mark 6).
2. Place the fruit in a single layer in an ovenproof dish, drizzle over the orange rind and juice and place in the oven for 10 minutes.
3. Mix all the other ingredients for the topping in a bowl.
4. Sprinkle the topping over the fruit and return to the oven for 10–12 minutes until golden.
5. Serve with a little ice cream or light crème fraîche.

CRANACHAN

This is a traditionally Scottish dessert. Many Scots still use the name crowdie cream because, in the past, a soft Scottish cheese called crowdie was used in the place of cream. You can use other fruit instead of raspberries, but the tartness of raspberries works very well. I've made it with frozen black cherries, but my dinner guests weren't so impressed.

You will need for 2 servings:
300 g (10 oz) raspberries
280 ml (10 fl oz) double cream
2 tablespoons good quality honey
2 tablespoons single malt whisky
2–3 tablespoons of oatmeal

Method:
1. Place the oatmeal in a dry pan and turn on the heat to simmer. Toast the oatmeal until it is golden brown. This process could take between 10–20 minutes.
2. Once the oatmeal is brown, turn off the heat and let it cool in the pan.
3. Place the cream in a bowl and whisk up until soft and thickened.
4. Add the honey and whisky and fold into the cream.

5. Reserving some of the best raspberries for decoration, add three or four to the bottom of each serving glass.
6. Add the rest of the raspberries to the cream mixture and fold in carefully, crushing a few to obtain a colouring to the cream.
7. Spoon the mixture into the serving glasses, then add a little more cream to the top to make an even base for the oatmeal.
8. Using a teaspoon, evenly sprinkle the oatmeal over the dessert. Add a raspberry for the finishing touch and chill for about three hours, or overnight.

Cranachan can be served on its own, or with double cream and more raspberries. You can also freeze the mixture in a container for a yoghurty ice cream, but use it quickly. No problem there, then!

I've also substituted crème fraîche and yoghurt instead of double cream, amending the quantities to suit diet and taste for various friends and family. Funnily enough, if I make a diabetic version for myself, with less honey and low fat yoghurt, it seems just as popular with everyone else!

QUICK CRANACHAN PUDDING

If you're really pushed for time then this recipe from Orkney saves a lot of the toasting and is a simpler version of the recipe above. You do need to think ahead though, for overnight soaking of the oats.

You will need:
  2 tablespoons medium oatmeal
  2 tablespoons runny honey
  2 tablespoons fresh orange or apple juice
  300 ml ($^1/_2$ pint) double or whipping cream, or thick yoghurt
  110 g (4 oz) raspberries, or mixed fruit, eg banana, stewed
    apple, plus a few raspberries

Method:
1. The day before; soak the oatmeal in the honey and fruit juice in a covered dish.
2. Whip the cream until stiff and fold in your chosen fruit to the oats.
3. Chill in the fridge for a short while, or serve semi-frozen.

HOT BLUEBERRY DESSERT

You will need:

> 4 tablespoons porridge oats
> 150 ml (5 fl oz) milk
> 1 tablespoon brown sugar
> squeeze of lemon juice
> 12 blueberries plus extra to garnish
> 3 tablespoons ricotta
> 1 tablespoon honey

Method:
1. Mix the porridge oats and milk together in a bowl. Microwave on high for 3 minutes and then allow to cool slightly.
2. Stir in the sugar and place a large spoonful of the porridge into a tall glass.
3. Cover with four blueberries, one tablespoon of ricotta and a drizzle of honey.
4. Repeat until you have used all the ingredients.
5. Garnish with extra blueberries and serve.

APPLE AND RASPBERRY PORRIDGE DESSERT

This seems to be a porridge dish too good for breakfast. Being served cold with cream, it is an ideal dessert during the raspberry season.

You will need:

1 eating apple, diced
1 teaspoon lemon juice
225 g (8 oz) raspberries
40 g (1$^1/_2$ oz or $^1/_2$ cup) oatmeal
3 cups water
1 cup milk
knob of butter
150 ml ($^1/_4$ pint cream)
1 tablespoon caster sugar
1 tablespoon brown sugar

Method:
1. Toss the apple in the lemon juice and cook until softened. Allow to cool.
2. Put oatmeal and water in a pan, stirring all the time.
3. Bring to the boil, add butter, stirring all the time and simmer until it thickens. Mix in the caster sugar and stand to cool.
4. When completely cool add the cream.
5. Add the fruit and mix well, saving a few raspberries for decoration.
6. Serve in small dishes and decorate with brown sugar and raspberries.

APPLE OAT BARS

Although given as a cake recipe, this gives quite a soft result. It could be served as a pudding, with custard or cream. It has the advantage of no added sugar or fats.

You will need:

225 g (8 oz) porridge oats
1 small apple
225 ml (8 fl oz) milk
120 g (4 oz) chopped dates or raisins
120 g (4 oz) coconut (optional)
1 teaspoon cinnamon
60 g (2 oz) flaked almonds

Method:
1. Preheat the oven to 180°C (350°F, gas mark 4) and grease a square baking tin.
2. Peel and grate, or finely chop, the apple.
3. Scatter $^1/_3$ of the oats into the baking tin and sprinkle $^1/_2$ the raisins or dates and coconut over the oats.
4. Place another $^1/_3$ of the oats over the raisins or dates with the apple and $^1/_2$ the cinnamon.
5. Pour over $^1/_2$ of the milk. Sprinkle on the remaining raisins and coconut then the rest of the oats.
6. Top off with cinnamon, milk and almonds.
7. Bake for 35—40 minutes and cool before cutting into squares or bars.

MAPLE BAKED APPLES
WITH TOASTED OATS AND ALMONDS

You will need:

2 apples, peeled, cored, and sliced
45 g (1$^1/_2$ oz) maple syrup
pinch cinnamon
pinch ground nutmeg
60 g (2 oz) rolled oats
60 g (2 oz) sliced almonds
1 tablespoon whole-wheat flour

Method:

1. Preheat oven to 200°C (400°F, gas mark 6).
2. Combine apples and 2 tablespoons of the maple syrup in a large non-stick frying pan over medium-high heat.
3. Sauté until the apples are tender and transfer to an oven proof dish.
4. In a small bowl, mix the remaining maple syrup, cinnamon, and nutmeg. Add the oats, almonds, and flour and mix well.
5. Spread the mixture over the apple slices and bake until the top is golden brown.

You can substitute firm peaches or pears for the apples.

OATMEAL AND YOGHURT CREAM DESSERT

You will need: **Makes 4 portions**

40 g (1¹/₂ oz) chopped almonds
40 g (1¹/₂ oz) oatmeal
25 g (1 oz) brown sugar
150 ml (5 fl oz) low fat natural yoghurt
150 ml (5 fl oz) double or whipping cream
grated rind and juice of ¹/₂ lemon or lime
1 tablespoon flaked, toasted almonds

Method:

1. Toast the oats with the chopped almonds in a frying pan, stirring until golden brown. Leave them to cool.
2. Mix the sugar with lemon or lime juice and stir in the yoghurt. Mix in the oats and nuts.
3. Whip the cream and fold into the mix.
4. Spoon into individual dishes or large wine glasses and chill. Just before serving, sprinkle with toasted almonds.

You can make this into a frozen yoghurt dessert by making a day ahead and freezing at stage 3 in a shallow tub until set. Scoop spoonfuls into glass dishes and sprinkle with nuts. Don't keep it too long in the freezer, though.

STEAMED OAT AND HONEY PUDDING

I'm sure this recipe would work equally well in a microwave, which would speed up the cooking time.

You will need:
450 ml ($^3/_4$ pint) milk
175 g (6 oz) porridge oats
50 g (2 oz) brown sugar
2 tablespoons honey
25 g (1 oz) butter or margarine
grated rind of 1 orange
$^1/_2$ teaspoon cinnamon
3 eggs, separated

Method:
1. Bring the milk to the boil and add the oats. Stir and cook gently for 5 minutes.
2. Beat in the honey, sugar, butter or margarine, orange rind and cinnamon. Remove from the heat and beat in the egg yolks.
3. Beat the egg whites until stiff and fold into the mixture.
4. Pour into a greased 1.2 litre (2 pint) pudding bowl and cover with greaseproof paper. Tie with string and steam in a pan of water for about 2 hours.
5. Turn onto a dish and serve with honey and cream.

BANANA, RAISIN AND OATMEAL PANCAKES

These pancakes are great with maple syrup, honey, marmalade, or even cottage cheese.

You will need: **Makes 6 pancakes**
140 g (5 oz) porridge oats
140 g (5 oz) plain flour
40 g (1.5 oz) golden brown sugar
1 teaspoon baking powder
pinch baking soda
pinch ground cinnamon
100 ml (3 fl oz) plain yogurt
100 ml (3 fl oz) milk

1 egg
1 ripe banana, mashed
140 g (5 oz) raisins
2 tablespoons melted butter
additional butter for cooking

Method:
1. Mix together the oats, flour, sugar and other dry ingredients in bowl.
2. Blend the yoghurt, milk and egg in another bowl.
3. Mix the dry ingredients into the yoghurt mixture until blended.
4. Fold in banana, raisins and melted butter.
5. Brush a non-stick griddle or pan with melted butter over a medium heat.
6. Working in batches, cook the pancakes until bubbles form on top and the bottoms are golden brown. Turn and cook for another minute or two.

FILLED OATMEAL SQUARES

This recipe uses tinned pie filling, so the amount of juice may vary. Be prepared to drain off some of the juice before adding to the undercrust, or thicken it with cornflour. You could make a cherry sauce to serve separately. Obviously, fresh cherries would be ideal.

You will need:
50 g (2 oz) sugar
150 g (5 oz) chopped walnuts
150 g (5 oz) old fashioned oats
80 g butter or margarine, softened
120 g (4 oz) plain flour
pinch of cinnamon
400 g (14 oz) can light cherry pie filling (drain off some of the juice)

Method:
1. Preheat oven to 200°C (400°F, gas mark 6).
2. Mix the sugar, walnuts, oats, butter and flour until crumbs form.

3. Press half of the crumbs into the bottom of a 20 cm (8 in) square baking dish.

4. Add the cinnamon to the cherry filling and spread over the crust.

5. Sprinkle the remaining crumbs over and press gently.

6. Bake for 20–25 minutes or until lightly browned. Cool on a rack and cut into squares.

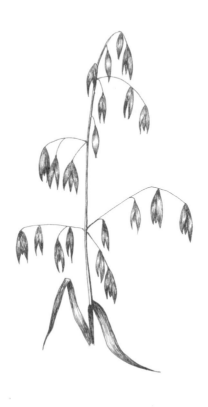

MISCELLANEOUS RECIPES

This section deals with a variety of ideas — some rather unusual. How adventurous are you feeling? There are also some recipes I came across for making porridge using other cereals.

OATMEAL SOUP

Using oats to thicken sauces, soups and stews is well documented and can also go towards making healthier versions of favourites. This soup is virtually fat free. You could toast the oatmeal in a dry pan over medium heat before adding to the soup.

You will need:

1 onion, sliced
225 g (8 oz) mushrooms, sliced
2 cloves garlic, finely chopped
80 g (3 oz) rolled oats
1 litre (2 pints) vegetable broth (or chicken broth)
1 large tin stewed tomatoes
1 small can tomato puree
seasoning
225 ml (8 fl oz) skimmed milk

Method:

1. Cook the onion, mushrooms and garlic in a little of the soup for about 5 minutes.
2. Stir in the oats, broth, tomatoes and tomato puree and bring to the boil.
3. Reduce the heat and simmer for 5 minutes. Season and stir in the milk.

CREAM OF ONION SOUP

This Scottish recipe has a very delicate flavour. Buttery white in colour, it looks lovely with a garnish of parsley or corriander on top.

You will need:

    1 large onion, chopped
    1 tablespoon butter or oil
    2 tablespoons medium oatmeal
    500 ml (1 pint) chicken or vegetable stock
    250 ml ($^1/_2$ pint) semi skimmed milk
    seasoning

Method:

1. Melt the butter in a saucepan. Add the onion and cook until soft but not brown.
2. Add oatmeal and seasoning and cook for a few minutes.
3. Add the stock slowly, stirring all the time. Bring to the boil, cover then simmer for 30 minutes.
4. Liquidise until smooth. Add the milk and heat through. Serve garnished with parsley or coriander leaves.

OATMEAL CLAY

Whatever you do, do not attempt to eat this creative concoction! It provides a no-cook, sturdy clay or playdough for sculpting. It dries very hard overnight and makes very pretty earthy-textured beads or models. For a smoother clay, put the oatmeal in the blender before mixing.

You will need:

    225g (8 oz) rolled oats (instant or old-fashioned)
    150g (5 oz) flour
    120 ml (4 fl oz) water
    food colouring

Method:

1. Mix the dry ingredients together.
2. Add the water slowly and adjust if too wet or dry. Add colouring of your choice.

PORRIDGE WITH SNAILS

This recipe could be described as posh nosh in some restaurants, although not being a fan of molluscs in any shape or location, I'd have to say that for me porridge with snails will have to dwell in the land of theory — even if there are snails at the bottom of my garden!

You will need:

Cooked snails:

    36 cleaned, edible snails
    1 small carrot
    1 small onion
    $1/2$ fennel bulb
    1 stick of celery
    50 g (2 oz) button mushrooms, finely sliced
    1 garlic clove
    2 bay leaves
    sprigs of thyme and rosemary
    25 g (1 oz) Parma ham (optional)

Porridge

    100 ml (4 fl oz) stock from cooking the snails
    30 g (2 oz) porridge oats
    snail butter (see below)
    cooked snails (see above)

Snail butter

    2 garlic cloves, peeled
    25g (1 oz) button mushrooms, finely chopped
    25g (1 oz) shallots, finely chopped
    100g (4 oz) butter, at room temperature
    1 tablespoon French mustard
    1 dessertspoon ground almonds
    $1/2$ teaspoon salt
    100g (4 oz) flatleaf parsley, chopped

Method:

1. Heat the butter in a frying pan, and sauté the mushrooms and shallots for 5 minutes until softened. Set aside for later.

2. Put the remaining butter ingredients in a food processor and purée until smooth. Mix in the mushrooms and shallots.

3. Harden the butter by rolling in greaseproof paper and placing in the fridge for several hours.

4. Cook the snails by adding them to a pan of boiling water. Skim the surface and reduce the heat to provide a gentle simmer.

5. Add the rest of the ingredients and simmer for about three hours.

6. Remove the snails and add the oats to the stock. Stir to absorb all the liquid and until the oats are cooked.

7. Allow to cool, then add half the snail butter. Season to taste.

To serve, spoon the porridge onto plates and top with a slice of Parma ham (optional). Top the porridge with the snails and the remaining snail butter. Enjoy!

FRUMENTY (WHEAT PORRIDGE)

Frumenty (also known as Furmenty) was used in medieval times as an accompaniment to meat dishes and also as a breakfast dish.

You will need:

> 275 g (10 oz) of kibbled wheat, bulgur (cracked wheat)
>   or ordinary wheat
> 1 litre (2 pints) water
> 150 ml (5 fl oz) meat or chicken stock
> 2 egg yolks, well beaten
> pinch of dried saffron strands (or pinch of turmeric)
> salt to taste

Note: it is much easier to use bulgur wheat.
Optional: fresh milk instead of stock. Much more palatable for breakfast.

Make the porridge in the normal way, by adding the wheat to the stock or milk, beaten with the egg yolks and the saffron or turmeric. Add the salt before serving.

STEAMED SKIRLIE (OATMEAL STUFFING)

You will need:

225 g (8 oz) Scottish Oatmeal
125 g (4 oz) Suet (or vegetable oil)
1 large onion, finely chopped
2–3 tbsp semi-skimmed milk
salt and pepper

Method:
1. Mix oatmeal and suet or vegetable oil and season.
2. Combine with chopped onion and milk.
3. Place in a pint pudding basin, cover and steam for one hour.

BOWSER'S RANCH-STYLE BEEF BONES

Makes a dark, textured, crunchy, meaty-flavoured biscuit for your four-legged family member. A meaty treat that dogs will love, helping them at the same time to maintain healthy teeth and gums. Makes about 80 using a small K-9 cutter.

You will need:

500 g (1 lb) lean ground beef
2 eggs, beaten
750 ml (3 cups) all purpose flour
250 ml (1 cup) quick cooking rolled oats
250 ml (1 cup) water

Method:
1. In a blender or food processor, combine beef and beaten eggs until well blended and set aside.
2. In a large mixing bowl, combine flour and rolled oats. Gradually mix in beef mixture with your hands, until well blended.
3. Add water and stir to form a sticky dough.
4. Divide dough into 2 balls, so it is easy to work with.

5. Knead each dough ball on a well floured surface, about 2 minutes, adding flour until the dough is no longer sticky.

6. With a rolling pin, roll out to between 1–1^1/$_2$ cm (^{1}/$_4$–^{1}/$_2$ in) thickness.

7. Cut with a K-9 biscuit cutter and place on a lightly greased baking tray.

8. Bake in the oven for one hour at 180°C (350°F, gas mark 4).

9. Cool on a rack and store at room temperature, in a container with a loose fitting lid.

CRUNCHY PEANUT BUTTER AND OATS SPREAD

You will need:

    150 g (5 oz) rolled oats
    300 g (10 oz) smooth peanut butter
    120 ml (4 oz) honey

Method:

1. Toast the oats by putting them in a dry frying pan over medium heat and stirring until browned.

2. Mix together the toasted oats, peanut butter and honey.

WHEAT PORRIDGE

You will need for 8 servings:

    120 g (4 oz) stone ground, whole-wheat flour
    1 litre (1^3/$_4$ pints) water
    1 pinch salt
    10 large dates, chopped
    3 tablespoons almonds, cut

Method:

1. Add salt to water and boil. Lower heat and add flour, stirring well until the desired thickness is reached.

2. Add the dates and almonds. Cook 20 minutes on low heat, stirring occasionally.

OATMEAL STOUT

There seem to be quite a variety of recipes for types of stout around, which include oats. One (American) recipe I came across includes a large amount of Belgian chocolate, which seems to be rather too alternative, or a little OTT for my liking!

Unfortunately the method sections deal with the primary fermentation, but then become vague. I include the ingredients for interest and expect dedicated beer brewers could fill in the gaps.

You will need: **Makes 5 gallons**

$1^1/_2$ kilo (3 lb) can dark malt extract syrup
450 g (1 lb) pale malt extract (dried)
450 g (1 lb) oatmeal
225 g (8 oz) brown sugar
450 g (1 lb) molasses
85 g (3 oz) hops
19 litres (5 gallons) water
1 packet yeast
300 g unbleached cane sugar or corn sugar (for priming)

Method:
Use a very big (stainless steel or enamelled) pot because you need to let the malt work on the starches and sugars while gradually increasing the temperature.

1. Put the oatmeal and the hops in separate cloth bags, or clean, old tights.
2. Bring 2 gallons of water to the boil, turn off the heat, add the oatmeal and let it steep for 1 hour.
3. Remove the oatmeal and dissolve all the malt sugar and molasses.

4. Add the bag of hops. Bring this wort to near boiling and simmer for at least an hour, then bring to a rolling boil. Be careful, as it will froth up briefly.

5. Continue the rolling boil for $^1/_2$ hour, then pour the wort into the primary fermentor. Add enough boiling water to the wort to reach the 5 gallon mark on your fermentor.

6. Add the yeast when the wort has cooled.

After going through the primary and secondary fermentation stages, add the priming sugar about 3 hours before bottling.

SUNFLOWER AND OAT BIRDFOOD

This will keep the cold at bay during the winter. Strictly for the birds, though.

You will need:

40 g (2 oz) quick oats
2 tablespoons sunflower seeds
2 tablespoons millet
2 tablespoons cornmeal
2 tablespoons whole-wheat flour
40 g (2 oz) peanut butter, smooth or crunchy
120 ml (4 fl oz) water

Method:
1. Mix all the ingredients very well — add more water if necessary to make a stiff dough.
2. Shape into balls and flatten. Bake at 130°C (250°F, gas mark $^1/_2$) for 20 minutes.

BANANA AND CHOCOLATE MILLET PORRIDGE

You will need per bowl:
    3 tablespoons millet flour
    120 ml (4 fl oz) water
    1 banana
    1 tablespoon cocoa powder
    pinch salt

Method:
1. Boil the flour and water until thick (about 5 minutes).
2. Cool and add cocoa powder, salt and mashed banana. Mix thoroughly.

HEALTHY FISH 'N' CHIPS

They say that fish and chips is the healthiest take away you can have, but if you make it at home it can be even better for you.

You will need:
    a fillet of your favourite white fish
    milk
    oatmeal
    porridge oats
    flour
    mixed herbs and pepper for seasoning

Method:
1. Mix together the flour, oatmeal, porridge oats and seasoning. Prepare you fillet of fish.
2. Dip the fish in the milk and then coat in the dry mixture of the flour, oatmeal, porridge oats and seasoning.
3. Shallow fry the fish in olive oil until the mixture has crisped up all over.
4. Serve with salad or peas and roasted potato wedges.

RELAXING OATY DRINK

This is a warming and relaxing drink, but at the same time, is stimulating.

You will need:

    200 ml water
    10 ml oatmeal
    2.5 ml brown sugar
    2.5 ml lemon juice
    1.25 ml ground ginger

Method:

1. Put the oatmeal, sugar and ginger into a mug or small jug. Mix with 15 ml of cold water taken from the 200 ml.
2. Add the lemon juice.
3. Boil the water and add to the mixture, stirring well until all is blended. The amounts of ginger and sugar may be varied according to taste.

INDEX